Perturbation Techniques in Mathematics, Physics, and Engineering

Athena Series

SELECTED TOPICS IN MATHEMATICS

Edwin Hewitt, *Editor*

Richard Bellman

The Rand Corporation

Perturbation Techniques in Mathematics, Physics, and Engineering

HOLT, RINEHART AND WINSTON, INC.

New York • Chicago • San Francisco • Toronto • London

To Nina,

Who Changed Day into Bellman

Preface

There are many difficulties encountered in the application of mathematical techniques to the study of scientific problems. Of these, one of the most frustrating is the fact that even simple equations need not possess simple solutions. Consequently, if we are really determined to extract meaning from analytic formulations of physical processes, we must resort to various types of approximation. Foremost among these is the technique of perturbation, the method, or rather methodology, which we shall concentrate upon in this volume.

The fundamental idea is to relate the unknown to the known by means of simple transitions. This is a comparative method, a procedure used throughout all intellectual domains. In the parlance of complex variable theory, we will employ analytic continuation.

There are, however, many ways of carrying out these ideas, including some inconvenient and incorrect ones.

In the first chapter, we study various examples of the general equation

$$L(u) + \epsilon N(u) = 0, \tag{1}$$

where $L(u) = 0$ is an equation that can be readily solved. The case where $L(u)$ is a linear algebraic equation furnishes an opportunity to demonstrate some of the versatility of the Lagrange expansion theorem. We then turn to the most important case—that where $L(u) = 0$ is a linear differential equation. This leads by easy stages to a discussion of the matrix exponential and to a brief excursion into the domain of Poincaré and Lyapunov. In this connection, we can illustrate an application of invariant imbedding. Subsequently, in discussing alternate perturbation techniques, we use dynamic programming.

Our attention, in the second chapter, is focused on obtaining periodic solutions of second-order nonlinear differential equations. Here, great care is necessary in applying perturbation techniques, as simple examples show. In addition to presenting the renormalization techniques of Lindstedt and Shohat, we shall present some new averaging techniques obtained in recent joint work with Richardson.

The concluding chapter is devoted to a consideration of various questions centering about the second-order linear differential equation

$$u'' + k^2(x)\, u = 0. \tag{2}$$

In order to obtain an approximate solution, we apply the WKB-Liouville

v

method, first in purely formal fashion and then in the physical context of wave propagation. In this way, we again make contact with invariant imbedding. We then turn to the subject of asymptotic series and their application to the approximate solution of linear differential equations.

As with all authors, we are well aware of the limitations of our selection of topics. Our defense is that it is manifestly impossible to penetrate deeply into any area or to range over any wide domain within the confines of a short monograph of this nature. What we have attempted to do is to introduce the reader to a plethora of problems, all interesting and all of scientific significance, to indicate a number of useful methods, some old, some new, and to furnish a guide to further reading. Many of the techniques we present have either been buried in the literature or else are so newly developed as to be available only in research papers.

The book is designed for pure and applied mathematicians, physicists, and engineers, and all others who are interested in obtaining numbers from equations. We assume a course in intermediate calculus and the rudiments of the theory of ordinary differential equations. Starting from this level, the material is self-consistent.

As usual, a number of friends have been imposed upon to read various chapters. Many useful ideas and comments are due to P. Brock, T. A. Brown, O. Gross, R. E. Kalaba, and S. Lehman. A particular vote of appreciation is due to J. M. Richardson. In addition to collaborating in the derivation of a number of the results and methods contained in the following pages, he very kindly allowed me to try out the material in a series of lectures at the Hughes Research Laboratories in Malibu, California.

R. B.

Santa Monica, California
September, 1963

Contents

*Perturbation Techniques
in Mathematics, Physics,
and Engineering*

[1]

Classical Perturbation Techniques

1. Introduction

There are major differences between the well-mapped world of the under-graduate and even the graduate university, and the uncharted regions of scientific research. The problems on examinations and in textbooks, in general, have relatively simple and straightforward answers obtained by means of clearly designated methods. The questions encountered in research are often neither clearly stated nor precisely formulated. Indeed, this is frequently the major part of the task. On the whole, simple answers rarely exist; no answers in the classical sense may exist at all, and there need not be any theories available that directly pertain to the problem.

As an additional ironic touch, in the few cases where the mathematical equations are explicitly soluble, the analytic representation may be unsuitable for either mathematical or physical interpretation, or for numerical evaluation. Simple examples of this frustrating phenomenon are the explicit solution of linear algebraic equations by means of Cramer's rule, and its limiting form, the Fredholm solution of linear integral equations; the solution of fifth-degree polynomial equations by means of elliptic functions; and the solution of linear differential equations with doubly periodic coefficients by means of doubly periodic functions.

In consequence, one of the major problems confronting the mathematician, after he has passed the first hurdle of achieving a reasonable analytic formulation of a physical process, is that of deriving useful and meaningful approximations to the solutions of the equations describing the process. In some cases, analytic ingenuity, alone or abetted by digital computers, will furnish the desired expressions; in other cases, a combination of "low cunning" and physical intuition will provide the essential key.

In still other cases, a completely new interpretation and formulation of the physical situation is required. A major obstacle at the start of any research is ignorance of where the real difficulties lie. The greater part of the time, only perseverance and plodding effort yield this vital information.

In this initial chapter, prior to a discussion of any more sophisticated devices, we wish to present the simplest and most useful of all approximation techniques: the expansion of a solution as a power series in a parameter—the

1

classical perturbation technique upon which much of the edifice of science rests.

2. The Fundamental Technique

The basic idea can be exhibited most easily in abstract terms. Subsequently, we shall apply it to the study of some representative algebraic, transcendental, and differential equations.

Suppose that we are required to solve the equation

$$F(u) = v, \tag{2.1}$$

which, for any of a variety of reasons, is inconvenient to tackle in its original form. It may, for example, be nonlinear, be linear but of high dimension, or possess stochastic elements in either linear or nonlinear form.

Let

$$L(u) = v \tag{2.2}$$

be an auxiliary equation that possesses a useful explicit solution

$$u = T(v), \tag{2.3}$$

in general, the unique solution of (2.2). In practice, this means that $L(u)$ is a *linear* operation on u; that is,

$$L(c_1 u_1 + c_2 u_2) = c_1 L(u_1) + c_2 L(u_2) \tag{2.4}$$

for any two functions u_1 and u_2 and scalars c_1 and c_2. Let us henceforth assume that L is linear.

Returning to (2.1), we write it in the form

$$L(u) + (F(u) - L(u)) = v. \tag{2.5}$$

Introducing the new function $N(u) = L(u) - F(u)$, we write (2.5) as

$$L(u) = v + N(u). \tag{2.6}$$

To facilitate our discussion of particular solutions of (2.6), we introduce a parameter ϵ and consider the new equation

$$L(u) = v + \epsilon N(u). \tag{2.7}$$

In some situations, the introduction of ϵ is solely a mathematical artifice that permits us to do various types of "bookkeeping" in a systematic fashion. For example, it allows us to group terms of comparable degrees of approximation in a methodical and convenient fashion. In a large number of situations, however, this parameter occurs naturally, representing such diverse physical quantities as Planck's constant h, a coupling coefficient, the intensity of a shock, the reciprocal of the speed of light c, or the amplitude of a forcing term.

It is quite natural and sensible, therefore, to begin with the study of those equations where ϵ is close to zero. Let us then look for a solution of (2.7) having the form

$$u = u_0 + \epsilon u_1 + \epsilon^2 u_2 + \cdots, \tag{2.8}$$

a power series in ϵ with coefficients that are independent of ϵ. Clearly, the leading term u_0, obtained upon setting $\epsilon = 0$, is a solution of the linear approximation

$$L(u_0) = v, \tag{2.9}$$

a solution that we shall write as $u_0 = T(v)$.

To obtain the subsequent coefficients, u_1, u_2, $\cdots$, in a systematic fashion, we substitute u as given by (2.8) into (2.7) and equate terms, obtaining thereby

$$L(u_0 + \epsilon u_1 + \epsilon^2 u_2 + \cdots) = v + \epsilon N(u_0 + \epsilon u_1 + \epsilon^2 u_2 + \cdots). \tag{2.10}$$

Since L is by assumption a *linear* operator, the left side becomes

$$L(u_0) + \epsilon L(u_1) + \epsilon^2 L(u_2) + \cdots. \tag{2.11}$$

Assuming that $N(u)$ is "analytic" in u so that we can expand the right side of (2.10) as a power series in ϵ, we have

$$N(u_0 + \epsilon u_1 + \epsilon^2 u_2 + \cdots) = N(u_0) + \epsilon N_1(u_0, u_1) + \epsilon^2 N_2(u_0, u_1, u_2) + \cdots, \tag{2.12}$$

where, as indicated, the coefficient of ϵ^k depends only upon the quantities u_0, u_1, u_2, $\cdots$, u_k. This is clearly the case if $N(u)$ is an ordinary polynomial in u, a particularly important situation. Combining the expansions of (2.11) and (2.12), and equating coefficients of ϵ, the single equation of (2.7) gives rise to the *infinite* system of equations

$$L(u_0) = v,$$

$$L(u_1) = N(u_0),$$

$$L(u_2) = N_1(u_0, u_1),$$

$$\vdots$$

$$L(u_{k+1}) = N_k(u_0, u_1, \cdots, u_k), \tag{2.13}$$

and so on.

The important point to observe is that this infinite system can be solved recursively; that is, the determination of u_k involves a knowledge of u_n for $0 \leq n \leq k - 1$. The first equation yields, upon referring to (2.3), the result

$$u_0 = T(v). \tag{2.14}$$

From the second, we derive the relation

$$u_1 = T(N(u_0)) = T(N(T(v))). \tag{2.15}$$

Continuing in this way, we see that we can express each u_k solely in terms of v.

The infinite series in (2.8), whose coefficients are determined in the foregoing fashion is called a *formal solution* of the original equation in (2.7). To obtain a formal solution of (2.6), we need only set $\epsilon = 1$.

EXERCISES

2.1. Find the first four terms of formal solutions of

(a) $u = a + \epsilon u^2$,

(b) $u = a + \epsilon u^k$,

(c) $u = a + \epsilon e^{bu}$,

(d) $\dfrac{du}{dt} = au - \epsilon u^2, \qquad u(0) = c,$

(e) $u(t) = f(t) + \epsilon \displaystyle\int_0^1 k(t, s)\, u(s)\, ds.$

2.2. Study the solutions of equations (a), (b), (c), (d), in the neighborhood of $\epsilon = \infty$. What kinds of formal solutions exist?

3. Discussion

What has preceded immediately conjures up a number of highly interesting, most important, and, as one might therefore expect, extremely difficult questions, which constitute the recurring and interwoven themes of our text, to wit:

1.   Under what conditions does the infinite series of (2.8) converge and actually represent a solution of (2.7)?

2. If the series converge, what estimates of the rate of convergence can we give, and what techniques can we use to accelerate the convergence?

3. If the formal series does not converge, can the partial sums or, more generally, the coefficient u_k be used nevertheless in some adroit fashion to yield analytic and numerical estimates for the solutions of (2.7)?

4. If no such formal series exists, what types of modifications can be made in the form of the series to ensure the existence of analogous expansions?

These are not easy questions to answer, and the results of any sophistication and rigor that do exist depend heavily upon the nature of the particular linear operator $L(u)$ and the nonlinear operator $N(u)$. Although the problems are obviously of paramount theoretical and practical import, and although a great deal of attention has been paid to their study, there exists no startlingly large collection of rigorously established results in this area. Taking this fact into account and simultaneously the restrictions on space of this monograph, we shall focus our attention almost exclusively upon methods, and soft pedal the proofs. In return for this freedom, we shall be able to describe a variety of powerful techniques that have worked quite well in applications. A number of references will be given for those who wish to examine the various methods for establishing some of these results rigorously, and we shall rely upon exercises to exhibit the versatility of these techniques.

Finally we are employing one of the fundamental techniques of mathematics, the *imbedding* method, or the method of *continuity*. In place of the original problem, we consider a family of problems generated by the value of the parameter ϵ. For $\epsilon = 0$, the problem is trivial; $\epsilon = 1$ yields the problem we wish to solve. Our aim has been to provide a transition from a problem easily resolved to one we wish to resolve.

It is not always the case that we want to reduce the problem to the consideration of linear rather than nonlinear equations. The theory of invariant imbedding, discussed in Section **15**, illustrates this. See also the discussion in G. Temple, "Linearization and Delinearization," *Proc. Intern. Cong. of Math.*, 1958.

An excellent expository paper discussing many types of nonlinear problems arising in physics and engineering is T. Von Karman, "The Engineer Grapples with Nonlinear Problems," *Bull. Am. Math. Soc.*, **46**, 615-683, 1940.

4. Lagrange Expansion

Perhaps the simplest equation upon which to use the foregoing algorithm is

$$u = a + \epsilon g(u), \tag{4.1}$$

where u is a scalar quantity and g is a scalar function. If $g(u)$ is an analytic function of u in the neighborhood of the point $u = a$ and $|\epsilon|$ is sufficiently small, we know by means of straightforward application of the elements of the theory of functions of a complex variable that there will be a unique solution of (4.1) that is an analytic function of ϵ in the neighborhood of $\epsilon = 0$, and that this solution has the form

$$u = a + \epsilon h_1(a) + \epsilon^2 h_2(a) + \cdots, \tag{4.2}$$

where the coefficients are dependent upon a. Although these coefficients of the powers of ϵ can be found by repeated differentiation in the usual way, this rather laborious and pedestrian approach reveals very little of the structure of the functions $h_k(a)$. It is remarkable that a quite elegant and relatively simple explicit formula exists for the determination of the terms of the foregoing expansion.

THEOREM (LAGRANGE EXPANSION). Let $f(z)$ and $g(z)$ be functions of z analytic on and inside a contour C surrounding $z = a$, and let ϵ satisfy the inequality

$$|\epsilon g(z)| < |z - a| \tag{4.3}$$

for all z on the perimeter of C. Then the equation in (4.1) has precisely one root in the interior of C, $u = u(a)$.

Let $f(z)$ be analytic on and inside C. Then

$$f(u) = f(a) + \sum_{n=1}^{\infty} \frac{\epsilon^n}{n!} \left(\frac{d}{da}\right)^{n-1} [f'(a)\, g(a)^n]. \tag{4.4}$$

The simplest way to derive this result is to use the Cauchy integral theorem. We have

$$f(u) = \frac{1}{2\pi i} \int_C \frac{f(w)\, (1 - \epsilon g'(w))\, dw}{w - a - \epsilon g(w)}, \tag{4.5}$$

where C is the contour mentioned above, which contains precisely one zero of $w - a - \epsilon g(w)$.

Using the expansion

$$\frac{1}{w - a - \epsilon g(w)} = \sum_{n=0}^{\infty} \frac{\epsilon^n g(w)^n}{(w - a)^{n+1}}, \tag{4.6}$$

and integrating term by term, we have

$$f(u) = \sum_{n=0}^{\infty} \frac{\epsilon^n}{2\pi i} \int_C \frac{f(w)\, g(w)^n\, dw}{(w - a)^{n+1}} - \sum_{n=0}^{\infty} \frac{\epsilon^{n+1}}{2\pi i} \int_C \frac{f(w)\, g(w)^n\, g'(w)\, dw}{(w - a)^{n+1}}. \tag{4.7}$$

Integrating each of the integrals in the second sum by parts, we obtain the stated result.

There are many elegant applications of this result, some of which are given in the following exercises.

EXERCISES

4.1. Use the Lagrange expansion theorem to obtain the power series expansions in powers of ϵ of the solutions of

(a) $u = a + \epsilon u^n$,

(b) $u = a + \epsilon e^{bu}$ (Ramanujan's equation),

(See S. M. Shah, "On a function of Ramanujan," *Am. Math. Monthly*, **63**, 407-408, 1956.)

(c) $u = a + \epsilon \sin u$ (the Kepler equation).

4.2. Derive (4.4) as an exercise in repeated differentiation directly from the usual Taylor series expansion.

4.3. If $u = g(x - ut)$, show that $u_t = - uu_x$, and hence derive the Lagrange expansion. This was the procedure used by Lagrange. (See E. Goursat and E. R. Hedrick, *A Course in Mathematical Analysis*, Boston: Ginn and Company, 1904, pp. 404-405.)

4.4. Use the expansion to study the solutions of the equation

$$(pz + q) e^z = rz + s.$$

(See E. M. Wright, "Solution of the equation $(pz + q) e^z = rz + s$," *Bull. Am. Math. Soc.*, **66**, 277-281, 1960.)

4.5. Starting with the equation $z = a + t(z^2 - 1)$, deduce that

$$\frac{1}{(1 - 4at + 4t^2)^{1/2}} = 1 + \sum_{n=1}^{\infty} \frac{t^n}{n!} \left(\frac{d}{da}\right)^n (a^2 - 1)^n,$$

and thus Rodrigues' result

$$P_n(z) = \frac{1}{2^n n!} \left(\frac{d}{dz}\right)^n (z^2 - 1)^n.$$

4.6. Starting with the relation $z = a + tz$, establish the expansion

$$\frac{e^{-a/(1-t)}}{(1 - t)} = e^{-a} + \sum_{n=1}^{\infty} \frac{t^n}{n!} \left(\frac{d}{da}\right)^n (e^{-a}a^n),$$

and thus the analogue of Rodrigues' result for Laguerre polynomials.

4.7. Derive the expansion

$$(1 - z)^a = \sum_{n=0}^{\infty} \frac{aw^n}{(a + bn)} \binom{a + bn}{n},$$

where $w = z/(1 + z)^b$ and $\binom{m}{n}$ is the binomial coefficient, and thus the generalization of the Vandermonde convolution due to Gould,

$$\sum_{k=0}^{n} \binom{a + bk}{k} \frac{a}{a + bk} \binom{e + b(n - k)}{n - k} \frac{c}{c + b(n - k)}$$

$$= \binom{a + c + bn}{n} \frac{a + c}{a + c + bn}.$$

(See M. Skalsky, "A Note on Vandermonde's Convolution," *Am. Math. Monthly*, **69**, 404-405, 1962.)

4.8. Establish the following result of Wronski: If $x = a$ is a solution of $\phi(x) + \lambda f(x) = 0$, then

$$F(x) = F(a) - \frac{\lambda f(a) F'(a)}{\phi(a)} + \frac{\lambda^2}{2!} \frac{1}{\phi'(a)^3} \begin{vmatrix} \phi'(a) & f(a)^2 F''(a) \\ \phi''(a) & (f(a)^2 F'(a))' \end{vmatrix} - \cdots.$$

BIBLIOGRAPHY AND DISCUSSION

The expansion of Lagrange is a special case of more general series due to Teixera and Burmann. For detailed discussions and further results see

P. A. Sturrock, "Generalization of the Lagrange Expansion with Applications to Physical Problems," *J. Math. and Phys.*, **1**, 405-408, 1960.

E. T. Whittaker and G. N. Watson, *Modern Analysis*, London: Cambridge University Press, 1935, Chapter VII.

5. Multidimensional Lagrange Expansion

There is a multidimensional extension of the expansion given in the preceding section that can be applied to the study of the solutions of a system of simultaneous equations of the form

$$u_i = a_i + e_i g_i(u_1, u_2, \cdots, u_N), \qquad i = 1, 2, \cdots, N. \tag{5.1}$$

Results of this nature were first obtained by Stieltjes, generalizing Lagrange's technique, but first published by Poincaré using his multidimensional version of Cauchy's residue theorem.

COMMENTS AND BIBLIOGRAPHY

A detailed discussion and derivation of multidimensional Lagrange expansions, together with an extensive set of references, will be found in

I. J. Good, "Generalizations to Several Variables of Lagrange's Expansion, with Applications to Stochastic Processes," *Proc. Cambridge Phil. Soc.*, **56**, 367-380, 1960.

For an interesting application to the derivation of a fundamental result in combinatorial analysis, see

I. J. Good, "A Short Proof of MacMahon's 'Master Theorem,' " *Proc. Cambridge Phil. Soc.*, **58**, 160, 1962.

An important representation of the real solution of a system of real equations was derived by Kronecker, generalizing some results of Gauss. For applications and further references, see

G. Birkhoff and O. D. Kellogg, " Fixed Points in Function Space," *Trans. Am. Math. Soc.*, **23**, 96-115, 1922.

Finally, let us note that Wiener's integral may be used to provide an explicit solution of various types of functional equations. See the excellent review article

I. M. Gelfand and A. M. Yaglom, "Integration in Functional Spaces and its Applications in Quantum Mechanics," *J. Math. and Phys.*, **1**, 48-68, 1960,

and

R. H. Cameron, "A Generalized Heat Flow Equation and a Corresponding Poisson Formula," *Ann. of Math.*, **59**, 434-462, 1954,

where many additional references can be found.

Results of this type are important since they can be used, like Cauchy's formula, to provide series expansions.

6. Linear Differential Equations

The linear differential equation of first order

$$\frac{du}{dt} + a(t)\,u = b(t), \qquad u(0) = c, \tag{6.1}$$

affords no challenge to the analyst since it possesses a simple, explicit solution

$$u = c \exp\left(-\int_0^t a(s)\, ds\right) + \exp\left(\int_0^t a(s)\, ds\right) \int_0^t \exp\left(\int_0^s a(r)\, dr\right) b(s)\, ds, \qquad (6.2)$$

from which all properties can be quickly and effortlessly deduced.

This representation is most easily derived by multiplying (6.1) through by the integrating factor $\exp\left(\int_0^t a(s)\, ds\right)$ and integrating between 0 and t. This is a particular application of the use of the adjoint equation, a device that is generally helpful in the study of linear equations.

The second-order linear differential equation

$$\frac{d^2u}{dt^2} + a(t)\frac{du}{dt} + b(t)\, u = 0, \qquad (6.3)$$

on the other hand, is only partially tame. It can be shown, not without some difficulty, that the general solution of (6.3) cannot be obtained in terms of a finite number of quadratures and elementary operations.

As a result of this rather surprising result, we face the problem of deriving simple approximate solutions that will enable us to deduce significant properties of the actual solution. The basic question is that of deducing structural features of the solution from structural properties of the coefficients. As we shall see subsequently, underlying physical processes will be of great aid.

EXERCISES

6.1. Show that the change of variable $u = \exp \int^t v\, ds$ converts the second-order linear differential equation

$$u'' + a(t)\, u' + b(t)\, u = 0$$

into the first-order equation

$$v' + v^2 + a(t)\, v + b(t) = 0,$$

a Riccati equation.

6.2. Let v_0 be a solution of

$$v' + v^2 + a^2 = 0,$$

and

$$v = v_0 + \epsilon v_1 + \epsilon^2 v_2 + \cdots$$

be a perturbation solution of

$$v' + v^2 + a^2 + \epsilon b(t) = 0.$$

Obtain in this way perturbation solutions of

$$u'' + (a^2 + \epsilon b(t))\, u = 0.$$

COMMENT AND BIBLIOGRAPHY

An excellent discussion of the solvability of a particular second-order linear differential equation, the Bessel function, in terms of elementary functions is contained in

G. N. Watson, *A Treatise on the Theory of Bessel Functions*, London: Cambridge University Press, 1944.

The theory of these matters was initiated by Liouville. His results were extended by Mordukhai-Boltovskoi, Ostrowski, and Ritt. See

I. Kaplansky, *An Introduction to Differential Algebra*, Paris: Hermann et Cie, 1957.

J. F. Ritt, *Integration in Finite Terms*, New York: Columbia University Press, 1948.

7. Linear Equations with Almost Constant Coefficients

To begin our investigations of second-order linear equations of the type occurring in (6.3) we consider the case where the coefficients $a(t)$ and $b(t)$ differ only slightly from constants over the t interval of interest. We write

$$\begin{aligned}
a(t) &= a + (a(t) - a),\\
b(t) &= b + (b(t) - b),
\end{aligned} \tag{7.1}$$

where, by assumption, $|\, a(t) - a\,|$ and $|\, b(t) - b\,|$ differ from zero by quantities that are small compared to a and b, and consider the new equation

$$\frac{d^2 u}{dt^2} + (a + \epsilon(a(t) - a))\frac{du}{dt} + (b + \epsilon(b(t) - b))\, u = 0, \tag{7.2}$$

involving the parameter ϵ. Here, ϵ has been artificially introduced, as explained above, to aid in obtaining a series approximation to the solution of (6.3).

Following the notation of Section 2, we may set

$$L(u) = \frac{d^2u}{dt^2} + a\frac{du}{dt} + bu, \qquad (7.3)$$

$$N(u) = (a - a(t))\frac{du}{dt} + (b - b(t))\, u.$$

Proceeding along the lines indicated in Section 2, our first task is to study the solution of the linear equation

$$L(u) = v, \qquad (7.4)$$

in our case the inhomogeneous second-order linear differential equation

$$\frac{d^2u}{dt^2} + a\frac{du}{dt} + bu = v. \qquad (7.5)$$

8. Inhomogeneous Linear Equations

Let us review the process of obtaining the general solution of the inhomogeneous equation

$$\frac{d^2u}{dt^2} + a(t)\frac{du}{dt} + b(t)\, u = v, \qquad (8.1)$$

in terms of the solutions of the homogeneous equation.

The simplest general technique involves an appeal to some results for linear vector-matrix equations, Sections 15 through 17. For the case of constant coefficients, the Laplace transform can be used. For the foregoing equation, an ingenious technique due to Lagrange, the method of *variation of parameters*, is perhaps the quickest and most elementary.

We shall take u_1 and u_2 to be two linearly independent solutions of the homogeneous equation

$$\frac{d^2u}{dt^2} + a(t)\frac{du}{dt} + b(t)\, u = 0, \qquad (8.2)$$

and seek to determine two functions, w_1 and w_2, such that the function

$$u = w_1u_1 + w_2u_2 \qquad (8.3)$$

will satisfy (8.1). The interesting point to note is that this technique is itself a perturbation technique that can be used in the study of other types of functional equations.

From (8.3), we obtain by differentiation

$$\frac{du}{dt} = w_1 \frac{du_1}{dt} + w_2 \frac{du_2}{dt} + \frac{dw_1}{dt} u_1 + \frac{dw_2}{dt} u_2 . \tag{8.4}$$

As a first condition upon w_1 and w_2, let us require that

$$\frac{dw_1}{dt} u_1 + \frac{dw_2}{dt} u_2 = 0, \tag{8.5}$$

so that the derivative of u has the simple form

$$\frac{du}{dt} = w_1 \frac{du_1}{dt} + w_2 \frac{du_2}{dt} , \tag{8.6}$$

Differentiating once again, we have

$$\frac{d^2u}{dt^2} = w_1 \frac{d^2u_1}{dt^2} + w_2 \frac{d^2u_2}{dt^2} + \frac{dw_1}{dt} u_1' + \frac{dw_2}{dt} u_2' , \qquad \left('= \frac{d}{dt}\right). \tag{8.7}$$

Combining these results,

$$v = \frac{d^2u}{dt^2} + a(t) \frac{du}{dt} + b(t) u$$

$$= w_1 \left(\frac{d^2u_1}{dt^2} + a(t) \frac{du_1}{dt} + b(t) u_1 \right) + w_2 \left(\frac{d^2u_2}{dt^2} + a(t) \frac{du_2}{dt} + b(t) u_2 \right)$$

$$+ \frac{dw_1}{dt} u_1' + \frac{dw_2}{dt} u_2' . \tag{8.8}$$

Since u_1 and u_2 are solutions of the linear homogeneous equation (8.2), the foregoing relation reduces to

$$\frac{dw_1}{dt} u_1' + \frac{dw_2}{dt} u_2' = v. \tag{8.9}$$

Equations (8.5) and (8.9) constitute two simultaneous linear equations for the quantities dw_1/dt and dw_2/dt. Solving, we have

$$\frac{dw_1}{dt} = \frac{-v(t) u_2}{W(u_1, u_2)}, \qquad \frac{dw_2}{dt} = \frac{v(t) u_1}{W(u_1, u_2)}, \tag{8.10}$$

where $W(u_1, u_2)$ (the Wronskian of u_1 and u_2), has the form

$$W(t) = W(u_1, u_2) = \begin{vmatrix} u_1 & u_2 \\ u_1' & u_2' \end{vmatrix}. \tag{8.11}$$

It was shown by Abel and Jacobi that $W(t)$ can be evaluated very easily in terms of the coefficients of (8.2). Using the rule for differentiating a determinant, we have

$$\frac{dW}{dt} = \begin{vmatrix} u_1' & u_2' \\ u_1' & u_2' \end{vmatrix} + \begin{vmatrix} u_1 & u_2 \\ u_1'' & u_2'' \end{vmatrix}$$

$$= \begin{vmatrix} u_1 & u_2 \\ -a(t)\,u_1' - b(t)\,u_1 & -a(t)\,u_2' - b(t)\,u_2 \end{vmatrix} = -a(t)\,W. \qquad (8.12)$$

Hence

$$W(t) = W(0)\exp\left[-\int_0^t a(s)\,ds\right]. \qquad (8.13)$$

If u_1 and u_2 are chosen to be a fundamental set of solutions specified by the initial conditions

$$u_1(0) = 1, \qquad u_1'(0) = 0,$$

$$u_2(0) = 0, \qquad u_2'(0) = 1, \qquad (8.14)$$

$W(0)$ has the value 1.

Returning to (8.10) and integrating, we have

$$w_1 = -\int_0^t v(s)\,u_2(s)\exp\left(\int_0^s a(s_1)\,ds_1\right) ds,$$

$$w_2 = \int_0^t v(s)\,u_1(s)\exp\left(\int_0^s a(s_1)\,ds_1\right) ds. \qquad (8.15)$$

Hence, the solution of

$$\frac{d^2u}{dt^2} + a(t)\frac{du}{dt} + b(t)\,u = v, \qquad u(0) = c_1, \qquad u'(0) = c_2, \qquad (8.16)$$

has the form

$$u = c_1 u_1 + c_2 u_2 + \int_0^t v(s)\exp\left(\int_0^s a(s)\,ds_1\right)[u_1(s)\,u_2(t) - u_2(s)\,u_1(t)]\,ds. \qquad (8.17)$$

EXERCISES

8.1. If u_1 is a solution of $u'' + a(t)\,u = 0$, obtain another solution and thus the general solution.

8.2. Generalize the result of (8.13) to the case of an nth order linear differential equation

$$\frac{d^n u}{dt^n} + a_1(t)\frac{d^{n-1}u}{dt^{n-1}} + \cdots + a_n(t)\,u = 0.$$

8.3. Extend the Lagrange method to the case of nth order linear differential equations.

8.4. If u_1 and u_2 are two functions with the requisite number of derivatives, show that

$$\begin{vmatrix} u & u' & u'' \\ u_1 & u_1' & u_1'' \\ u_2 & u_2' & u_2'' \end{vmatrix} = 0$$

is a linear differential equation with two particular solutions, u_1 and u_2.

8.5. Show that

$$\frac{d^2u}{dt^2} + a_1(t)\frac{du}{dt} + a_2(t)\,u = \frac{W}{u_1}\frac{d}{dt}\left(\frac{u_1^2}{W}\frac{d}{dt}\left(\frac{u}{u_1}\right)\right),$$

where u_1 and u_2 are two linearly independent solutions of the homogeneous equation and W is the Wronskian of u_1 and u_2. (For proof and generalization, see G. Polyà and G. Szegö, *Aufgaben und Lehrsätze aus der Analysis*, Vol. II, New York: Dover Publications, 1945, p. 113. For an application, see E. F. Beckenbach and R. Bellman, *Inequalities*, Ergebnisse der Math., Berlin: Springer-Verlag, 1961.)

COMMENTS AND BIBLIOGRAPHY

For further results, see

R. Bellman, *Stability Theory of Differential Equations*, New York: McGraw-Hill Book Company, Inc., 1954.

———, *Introduction to Matrix Analysis*, New York: McGraw-Hill Book Company, Inc., 1960.

9. Linear Perturbation Series—I

With the aid of the foregoing relation (8.17), we can now present a systematic technique for obtaining approximate solutions of the equation

$$\frac{d^2u}{dt^2} + (a(t) + \epsilon a_1(t))\frac{du}{dt} + (b(t) + \epsilon b_1(t))\,u = 0,$$

$$u(0) = c_1, \qquad u'(0) = c_2, \tag{9.1}$$

where ϵ is a parameter, which we assume to be small. Write

$$u = u_0 + \epsilon u_1 + \epsilon^2 u_2 + \cdots, \tag{9.2}$$

and let the initial conditions hold *uniformly* in ϵ so that

$$u_0(0) = c_1, \qquad u_0'(0) = c_2,$$
$$u_i(0) = 0, \qquad u_i'(0) = 0, \qquad i \geq 1. \tag{9.3}$$

This is merely a matter of convenience, and need not always be the case.

Substituting the series solution of (9.2) in (9.1) and equating coefficients of powers of ϵ, we obtain the series of equations

$$\frac{d^2 u_0}{dt^2} + a(t)\frac{du_0}{dt} + b(t)\,u_0 = 0,$$

$$\frac{d^2 u_1}{dt^2} + a(t)\frac{du_1}{dt} + b(t)\,u_1 = -\left(b_1(t)\frac{du_0}{dt} + b_2(t)\,u_0\right), \tag{9.4}$$

$$\vdots$$

The function $u_0(t)$ is determined by the unperturbed equation, and taken to be known. We can solve for u_1 in terms of u_0 using (8.17), u_2 in terms of u_1 and thus in terms of u_0 and so on. Hence, we possess a systematic technique for deriving the coefficients in the expansion of (9.2). In many situations, this straightforward technique is sufficient for analytic and numerical purposes. In many other situations, however, more sophisticated techniques are required. Some of these will be presented in the following pages.

10. Linear Perturbation Series—II

An alternate approach that is a bit more elegant and of broader significance is the following. Write the original equation (9.1) in the form

$$\frac{d^2 u}{dt^2} + a(t)\frac{du}{dt} + b(t)\,u = -\epsilon\left(a_1(t)\frac{du}{dt} + b_1(t)\,u\right),$$

$$u(0) = c_1, \qquad u'(0) = c_2, \tag{10.1}$$

and use the formula of (8.17) regarding the right-hand side as an inhomogeneous term. We obtain

$$u = c_1 u_1 + c_2 u_2 + \epsilon \int_0^t k(t,s)\left[a_1(s)\frac{du}{ds} + b_1(s)\,u\right]ds, \tag{10.2}$$

where u_1 and u_2 are particular solutions of the homogeneous equation with the respective initial values $u_1(0) = 1$, $u_1'(0) = 0$, and $u_2(0) = 0$, $u_2'(0) = 1$, where the kernel $k(t, s)$ is given by the expression

$$k(t, s) = - \exp \left(\int_0^s a(s_1) \, ds_1 \right) [u_1(s) \, u_2(t) - u_2(s) \, u_1(t)], \qquad (10.3)$$

a function that we take to be known. Integrating by parts to eliminate the term in du/ds, we have

$$u = c_1 u_1 + c_2 u_2 + \epsilon[k(t, s) \, a_1(s) \, u]_0^t$$
$$+ \epsilon \int_0^t u(s) \left[k(t, s) \, b_1(s) - \frac{d}{ds} \left(k(t, s) \, a_1(s) \right) \right] ds. \qquad (10.4)$$

We can thus write, simplifying our notation,

$$u = w(t) + \epsilon \int_0^t k_1(t, s) \, u(s) \, ds, \qquad (10.5)$$

where

$$w(t) = c_1 u_1 + c_2 u_2 - \epsilon c_1 k(t, 0) \, a_1(0),$$

$$k_1(t, s) = k(t, s) \, b_1(s) - \frac{d}{ds} \left(k(t, s) \, a_1(s) \right). \qquad (10.6)$$

This is an integral equation for the unknown function u, more precisely, a Volterra integral equation.

To obtain u, we employ the simple technique of repeated substitution, a classical procedure:

$$u = w(t) + \epsilon \int_0^t k_1(t, s) \left[w(s) + \epsilon \int_0^s k_1(s, s_1) \, u(s_1) \, ds_1 \right] ds$$
$$= w(t) + \epsilon \int_0^t k_1(t, s) \, w(s) \, ds + \epsilon^2 \int_0^t k_1(t, s) \left(\int_0^s k_1(s, s_1) \, w(s_1) \, ds_1 \right) ds + \cdots. \qquad (10.7)$$

The resulting series is the Liouville-Neumann series solution for the integral equation of (10.5). Using the expression for $w(t)$, it is easy to pick out the coefficient of ϵ^n.

EXERCISES

10.1. Consider the following sequence of successive approximations to the solution of (10.5):

$$u_0 = w(t),$$

$$u_1 = w(t) + \epsilon \int_0^t k_1(t, s) \, u_0(s) \, ds,$$

$$u_2 = w(t) + \epsilon \int_0^t k_1(t, s) \, u_1(s) \, ds,$$

and so on. Show that $u_n(t)$ converges uniformly to the solution $u(t)$ in any t interval, $[0, t_0]$, within which $|k_1(t, s)| \leq k(t)$ where

$$\int_0^{t_0} k(t) \, dt \qquad \text{and} \qquad \int_0^{t_0} |w(t)| \, k(t) \, dt$$

exists. Hence establish the convergence of the perturbation series (10.7) for *all* ϵ.

10.2. What is the corresponding result for the Fredholm equation

$$u(t) = w(t) + \epsilon \int_0^1 k(t, s) \, u(s) \, ds.$$

10.3. Consider the equation

$$\epsilon \frac{du}{dt} + u = a(t).$$

Formally we have

$$u = a(t) - \epsilon \frac{du}{dt}$$

$$= a(t) - \epsilon \frac{da}{dt} + \epsilon^2 \frac{d^2u}{dt^2}$$

$$= a(t) - \epsilon \frac{da}{dt} + \epsilon^2 \frac{d^2a}{dt^2} \cdots.$$

Show that this process yields a *particular solution* if $a(t)$ is a polynomial in t. What happens if $a(t) = 1/t$?

Using the explicit solution, obtain the connection between the formal series above and particular solutions in general. (Subsequently, when we discuss asymptotic series, this relation will be made precise.)

DISCUSSION

The conversion of a differential equation into an integral equation is one of the most powerful devices available in connection with the study of approximate solutions—and one of the few standard techniques. Its potency is due

to the fact that integration is a smoothing operation, while differentiation accen-
tuates small variations in value. If $u(t)$ and $v(t)$ are close together, in the sense
that $\max_t | u(t) - v(t) |$ is small, the integrals

$$\int_0^t u(s)\, ds \qquad \text{and} \qquad \int_0^t v(s)\, ds$$

will be comparable in value, but the derivatives du/dt and dv/dt may
be arbitrarily far apart. Consider Fig. 1 (for example, $u(t) = 1/(t + 1)$, $u(t) =$
$1/(t + 1) + \epsilon \sin e^t$).

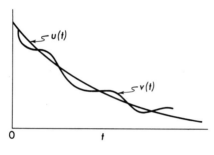

Fig. 1

Consequently, when carrying out successive approximations, we always
prefer integral operators to differential operators.

On the other hand, let us note that if we are interested in numerical solution
by way of digital or analogue computers, then we strongly prefer differential
operators to integral operators.

Subsequently, we shall discuss various ways of speeding up the convergence
of the Liouville-Neumann series.

11. Two-point Boundary-value Problems

So far, we have considered second-order linear differential equations

$$\frac{d^2u}{dt^2} + a(t)\frac{du}{dt} + b(t)\, u = 0, \tag{11.1}$$

where the solution was specified by initial values

$$u(0) = c_1, \qquad u'(0) = c_2. \tag{11.2}$$

In many important situations, this is not the case. Frequently, in the study of variational problems, and in mathematical physics, we encounter equations whose solutions are specified by values at two points, say

$$u(0) = c_1, \qquad u(1) = c_2, \tag{11.3}$$

and, sometimes, there are conditions at intermediate points as well.

The analytic solution is direct. We shall let u_1 and u_2 be the two principal solutions; that is,

$$u_1(0) = 1, \qquad u_1'(0) = 0,$$

$$u_2(0) = 0, \qquad u_2'(0) = 1, \tag{11.4}$$

and write

$$u = c_1 u_1 + c_3 u_2 , \tag{11.5}$$

where c_3 is an unknown constant determined by the condition at $t = 1$,

$$c_2 = u(1) = c_1 u_1(1) + c_3 u_2(1). \tag{11.6}$$

Hence

$$c_3 = \frac{c_2 - c_1 u_1(1)}{u_2(1)}. \tag{11.7}$$

We see that a solution exists and is unique, provided that $u_2(1) \neq 0$. If $u_2(1) = 0$, there is no solution unless $c_2 - c_1 u_1(1) = 0$. If this condition is satisfied, there is a one-parameter family of solutions given by (11.5), with c_3 an arbitrary parameter.

We see then that the study of solutions of (11.1) satisfying the boundary conditions

$$u(0) = 0, \qquad u(1) = 0, \tag{11.8}$$

is of importance. Clearly $u = 0$ is a solution. Are there other solutions?

Once again it is useful to introduce a parameter λ and ask the following more general question: for what values of λ, if any, does a nontrivial solution

$$\frac{d^2u}{dt^2} + a(t)\frac{du}{dt} + b(t)\,u + \lambda u = 0 \tag{11.9}$$

exist satisfying the boundary conditions of (11.8)?

Questions of this type were first investigated by Sturm and Liouville in the early nineteenth century, and hence equations of this type are called Sturm-Liouville equations. The values of λ are called *characteristic values*, or *eigenvalues* (a peculiar hybrid word), and the associated solutions are called *characteristic functions* or *eigenfunctions*.

EXERCISES

11.1. Consider the equation

$$u'' + \lambda u = 0, \qquad u(0) = u(1) = 0.$$

Show that nontrivial solutions exist if and only if $\lambda = n^2\pi^2$, $n = 1, 2, \cdots$, and that these solutions are $u_n = \sqrt{2} \sin n\pi t$, when normalized by the condition

$$\int_0^1 u_n^2 \, dt = 1.$$

11.2. Show that the foregoing equation is the Euler equation associated with the problem of minimizing

$$\int_0^1 u'^2 \, dt$$

over all u subject to the conditions $u(0) = u(1) = 0$ and

$$\int_0^1 u^2 dt = 1,$$

with λ playing the role of a Lagrange multiplier.

11.3. Consider the linear differential equation

$$u'' + \lambda a(t)\, u = 0, \qquad u(0) = u(1) = 0,$$

where we suppose that $0 < a^2 \le a(t) \le b^2 < \infty$. Let $v(t)$ be the solution specified by the initial conditions $v(0) = 0$, $v'(0) = 1$. Show that

$$v(t) = t + \sum_{n=1}^{\infty} \lambda^n u_n(t),$$

where

$$u_0(t) = t,$$

$$u_n(t) = -\int_0^t (t - s)\, u_{n-1}(s)\, a(s)\, ds,$$

is an expansion valid for *all* λ for $0 \le t \le 1$.

Show that the solutions of the equation $v(1) = 0$ are the required characteristic values, $\lambda_1, \lambda_2, \cdots$.

11.4. Show that

$$f(\lambda) = 1 + \sum_{n=1}^{\infty} \lambda^n u_n(1) = \sum_{i=1}^{\infty} \left(1 - \frac{\lambda}{\lambda_i}\right),$$

and that all of the λ_i are real and positive. If

$$\log f(\lambda) = \sum_{k=1}^{\infty} c_k \lambda^k,$$

show that

$$n u_n = n c_n + \sum_{k=1}^{n-1} k c_k u_{n-k}.$$

11.5. If

$$b_k = \sum_{i=1}^{\infty} \frac{1}{\lambda_i^k}, \qquad k = 1, 2, \cdots,$$

show that

$$\frac{b_k}{b_{k+1}} > \lambda_1 > \frac{1}{b_k^{1/k}}, \qquad k = 1, 2, \cdots.$$

Prove that the sequence $\{b_k/b_{k+1}\}$ is monotone decreasing, that the sequence $\{1/b_k^{1/k}\}$ is monotone increasing and that

$$\lambda_1 = \lim_{k \to \infty} \frac{b_k}{b_{k+1}} = \lim_{k \to \infty} \frac{1}{b_k^{1/k}}.$$

11.6. Obtain analogous results for the products $\Pi_{i=1}^{n} \lambda_i$. (For these results and an application to the Bessel equation $u'' + \lambda(1 + t) u = 0$, see R. Bellman, "On the Determination of Characteristic Values for a Class of Sturm-Liouville Problems," *Illinois J. Math.*, **2**, 577-585, 1958.)

11.7. Use Exercise 11.2, or otherwise, to show that the smallest characteristic value of the equation of Exercise 11.3 can be written

$$\lambda_1 = \min_u \left[\frac{\displaystyle\int_0^1 u'^2 dt}{\displaystyle\int_0^1 a(t) u^2 dt} \right],$$

where the minimum is over functions assuming the boundary values $u(0) = u(1) = 0$. Hence

$$\lambda_1 \leq \left[\frac{\displaystyle\int_0^1 u'^2 dt}{\displaystyle\int_0^1 a(t) u^2 dt} \right]$$

for *all* such functions.

COMMENTS AND BIBLIOGRAPHY

For an elegant unification of a number of variational principles important in mathematical physics, see

S. Altschuler, "Variational Principles for the Wave Function in Scattering Theory," *Phys. Rev.*, **109**, 1830-1836, 1958.

For a different variational approach based upon quasilinearization, see

F. Calogero, "A Note on the Riccati Equation," *J. Math. and Phys.*, to appear.
———, "A Variational Principle for Scattering Phase Shifts," *Nuovo Cimento*, to appear.
———, "The Scattering of a Dirac Particle on a Central Scalar Potential," *Nuovo Cimento*, to appear.

Relevant papers for quasilinearization are

R. Bellman, "Functional Equations in the Theory of Dynamic Programming—V: Positivity and Quasi-linearity," *Proc. Nat. Acad. Sci. US*, **41**, 743-746, 1955.
R. Kalaba, "On Nonlinear Differential Equations, the Maximum Operation, and Monotone Convergence," *J. Math. and Mech.*, **8**, 519-574, 1959.

For a detailed discussion of the equation $u'' + uf(u, \lambda, t) = 0$, subject to two-point boundary-value conditions, see

R. M. Moroney, "A Class of Characteristic-value Problems," *Trans. Am. Math. Soc.*, **102**, 446-470, 1962.

12. Perturbation Techniques—I

Let us now examine the problem of obtaining characteristic values and characteristic functions of the perturbed problem in terms of solutions of the original. This is a quite difficult and involved question, which we shall discuss only at the simplest level.

It is sufficient to illustrate our procedures with the simple equation

$$u'' + (\lambda + \epsilon b(t)) u = 0, \tag{12.1}$$

subject to the boundary conditions

$$u(0) = u(1) = 0. \tag{12.2}$$

If $\epsilon = 0$, the characteristic values are $\lambda_n = n^2\pi^2$, $n = 1, 2, \cdots$, and a set of normalized associated characteristic functions are $u_n = \sin n\pi t/n\pi$, $n = 1, 2, \cdots$.

We use the new normalization condition, $u'(0) = 1$, for reasons of convenience below. Let us see if we can find nearby characteristic values and nearby functions for small ϵ. We shall write (12.1) in the form

$$u'' + \lambda u = -\epsilon b(t) u, \tag{12.3}$$

and adjoin to the boundary conditions of (12.2) the additional condition $u'(0) = 1$. The fundamental solutions u_1 and u_2 of the homogeneous equation are

$$u_1 = \cos t \sqrt{\lambda}, \qquad u_2 = \frac{\sin t \sqrt{\lambda}}{\sqrt{\lambda}}. \tag{12.4}$$

Using (8.17), we convert (12.3) into the integral equation

$$u = \frac{\sin t \sqrt{\lambda}}{\sqrt{\lambda}} + \int_0^t \left[(\cos s \sqrt{\lambda}) \left(\frac{\sin t \sqrt{\lambda}}{\sqrt{\lambda}} \right) \right.$$

$$\left. - \left(\frac{\sin s \sqrt{\lambda}}{\sqrt{\lambda}} \right) (\cos t \sqrt{\lambda}) \right] [-\epsilon b(s) u(s)] \, ds, \tag{12.5}$$

or simplifying,

$$u = \frac{\sin t \sqrt{\lambda}}{\sqrt{\lambda}} - \frac{\epsilon}{\sqrt{\lambda}} \int_0^t b(s) \sin \sqrt{\lambda} \, (t - s) \, u(s) \, ds. \tag{12.6}$$

Setting $t = 1$, we obtain the transcendental equation

$$0 = \sin \sqrt{\lambda} - \epsilon \int_0^1 b(s) \sin \sqrt{\lambda} \, (1 - s) \, u(s) \, ds \tag{12.7}$$

for the determination of the characteristic values of λ.

Standard results of the theory of functions of a complex variable can now be used to show that if ϵ is small the new nth characteristic value has the form

$$\lambda_n = n^2 \pi^2 + \epsilon a_{1n} + \epsilon^2 a_{2n} + \cdots, \tag{12.8}$$

where the coefficients a_{in} are independent of ϵ. Returning to (12.5), one can by means of iteration of the type used in (10.7) obtain corresponding series for the nth characteristic function

$$u_n = \frac{\sin n\pi t}{n\pi} + \epsilon u_{1n}(t) + \epsilon^2 u_{2n} + \cdots. \tag{12.9}$$

The method we have presented is quite useful in the study of ordinary differential equations, but not as applicable to the treatment of the corresponding questions for partial differential equations and other types of functional equations.

13. Perturbation Techniques—II

As previously noted, the solutions of

$$u'' + \lambda u = 0, \qquad u(0) = u(1) = 0, \tag{13.1}$$

are nontrivial if, and only if, λ assumes one of the characteristic values, $\lambda = \pi^2, 4\pi^2, 9\pi^2, \cdots$. We choose as the associated characteristic functions the sequence

$$u_n(t) = \sqrt{2} \sin n\pi t, \tag{13.2}$$

where the coefficient $\sqrt{2}$ has been inserted to normalize subject to the condition

$$\int_0^1 u_n^2(t)\, dt = 1. \tag{13.3}$$

It turns out that this is a convenient normalization for the method we wish to employ.

Let us then look for a solution of

$$u'' + (\lambda + \epsilon b(t))\, u = 0, \qquad u(0) = u(1) = 0, \tag{13.4}$$

having the form

$$u = u_n + \epsilon \sum_{k \neq n} a_{kn} u_k + O(\epsilon^2), \tag{13.5}$$

$$\lambda = n^2\pi^2 + \epsilon\delta_n + O(\epsilon^2). \tag{13.5}$$

There is no need to normalize u if $\epsilon \ll 1$.

Expanding the term $b(t)\, u$ in an orthogonal series in terms of the u_k, a Fourier series in this case, we write

$$b(t)\, u = \sum_{k=1}^{\infty} b_k u_k , \tag{13.6}$$

where, by virtue of the orthonormal property of $\{u_k(t)\}$,

$$b_k = \sqrt{2} \int_0^1 b(t)\, u\, u_k(t)\, dt$$

$$= \sqrt{2} \int_0^1 b(t)\, u_n\, u_k(t)\, dt + O(\epsilon), \tag{13.7}$$

upon using (13.5).

Substituting the expressions of (13.5) in the equation of (13.4), we have

$$
-\left[\pi^2 n^2 u_n + \epsilon \pi^2 \sum_{k \neq n} k^2 a_{kn} u_k\right] + (n^2 \pi^2 + \epsilon \delta_n)\left(u_n + \epsilon \sum_{k \neq n} a_{kn} u_k\right)
$$

$$
+ \epsilon \left(\sum_{k=1}^{\infty} b_k u_k\right) = 0(\epsilon^2). \tag{13.8}
$$

Equating coefficients of ϵ, we have the desired relations

$$
\delta_n = - b_n = - \sqrt{2} \int_0^1 b(t)\, u_n^2\, dt = - 2\sqrt{2} \int_0^1 b(t) \sin^2 n\pi\, dt, \tag{13.9}
$$

$$
a_{kn} = - \frac{b_k}{\pi^2(n^2 - k^2)}, \qquad k \neq n, \tag{13.9}
$$

to terms which are $0(\epsilon)$.

Thus, the required expansions are

$$
u = u_n - \epsilon \sum_{k \neq n} \frac{b_k u_k}{(n^2 - k^2)\,\pi} + 0(\epsilon^2),
$$

$$
\lambda_n = \pi^2 n^2 - \epsilon b_n + 0(\epsilon^2), \tag{13.10}
$$

where the sequence $\{b_k\} = \{b_{kn}\}$ is given by the expression

$$
b_{kn} = 2\sqrt{2} \int_0^1 b(t) \sin n\pi t \sin k\pi t\, dt. \tag{13.11}
$$

Perturbation expansions of the foregoing type play an important role in quantum mechanics and throughout all of mathematical physics.

EXERCISES

13.1. Obtain the expansions of u and λ_n to terms in $0(\epsilon^3)$.

13.2. Let A and B be symmetric matrices, both positive definite. Use procedures analogous to those above to obtain perturbation series for the characteristic values and vectors of $A + \epsilon B$ in terms of those for A.

13.3. Extend the foregoing analysis to the general second order equation

$$
\frac{d}{dt}\left(p(t)\frac{du}{dt}\right) + (\lambda q(t) + r(t))\, u = 0,
$$

$$
u(0) = u(1) = 0.
$$

13.4. As noted in Exercise 11.7, the smallest characteristic value of $u'' + \lambda a(t) u = 0$, $u(0) = u(1) = 0$, under appropriate conditions on $a(t)$, is given by the relation

$$\lambda_1 = \min \left[\frac{\int_0^1 u'^2 \, dt}{\int_0^1 a(t) \, u^2 \, dt} \right].$$

Let μ_1 be the corresponding smallest characteristic value of

$$u'' + \lambda(a(t) + \epsilon b(t)) u = 0,$$

with the same boundary conditions, and let u_1 and v_1 be the respective characteristic functions, normalized by the conditions

$$\int_0^1 u_1^2 \, dt = \int_0^1 v_1^2 \, dt = 1.$$

Then

$$\lambda_1 \le \frac{\int_0^1 v'^2 \, dt}{\int_0^1 a(t) \, v_1^2 \, dt},$$

$$\mu_1 \le \frac{\int_0^1 u_1^2 \, dt}{\int_0^1 (a(t) + \epsilon b(t)) \, u_1^2 \, dt}.$$

From this deduce upper and lower bounds for μ_1 in terms of u_1 and λ_1.

This method is a particular example of what has been called "transplantation" by Polya and Schiffer and can be used in the study of many perturbation problems involving variational matters. See, for example,

R. Bellman, "Functional Equations in the Theory of Dynamic Programming—VI: A Direct Convergence Proof," *Ann. Math.*, **65**, 215-223, 1957.

G. Polya and M. Schiffer, "Convexity of Functionals by Transplantation (with an appendix by Heinz Helfenstein)," *J. Anal. Math.*, **3**, 245-346, 1954.

13.5. What types of perturbation expansions are valid if A has a multiple characteristic root? Consider the quadratic polynominal $(\lambda - 1)^2 + \epsilon\lambda = 0$ first. We have stayed clear of the difficult, but quite important, problems involving cases where A has multiple characteristic roots, or where the perturbation induces a continuous spectrum in place of the original discrete spectrum, because of the higher level of difficulty. For this latter, see

K. O. Friedrichs and P. A. Rejto, "On a perturbation through which a discrete spectrum becomes continuous," *Comm. Pure Appl. Math.*, **15**, 219-235, 1962.

14. Perturbation in General

So far we have considered only one simple type of variation of the equation, that of change of the coefficients in a linear equation. There are many other interesting and significant changes in structure, such as addition of nonlinear terms, perturbation of initial conditions, and variation of the interval of interest.

In Section 19, we shall discuss some of the effects of nonlinearity. It turns out that perturbation of initial or boundary values is rather simple to handle, but variation of the interval requires some effort.

EXERCISES

14.1. Given the equation

$$u'' = g(u, u', t), \qquad u(0) = c_1, \qquad u'(0) = c_2,$$

with the solution $u = u(t, c_1, c_2)$, show that $\partial u/\partial c_1 = w$ satisfies the equation

$$w'' = g_u w + g_{u'} w', \qquad w(0) = 1, \qquad w'(0) = 0.$$

14.2. Given the equation

$$u'' = g(u, u', t, \epsilon), \qquad u(0) = c_1, \qquad u'(0) = c_2,$$

show that $w = \partial u/\partial \epsilon$ satisfies the equation

$$w'' = g_u w + g_{u'} w' + g_\epsilon.$$

15. Invariant Imbedding

Fundamental physical processes are the reflection of waves or particles from strata of finite thickness or transmission through these regions. From both the experimental and theoretical point of view, the dependence of the intensities of reflected and transmitted waves or fluxes on the thickness of the medium is crucial. This dependence can be studied analytically in several ways. Here we shall use the perturbation techniques developed in the preceding sections to derive results that could be derived directly from a consideration of the physical process using the theory of invariant imbedding. A number of references to applications of the techniques of this theory will be found at the end of the section.

An idealized version of neutron transport in a one-dimensional rod of length x, leads, under appropriate assumptions, to equations of the form

$$\frac{du}{dz} = g(u, v), \qquad u(0) = 0,$$

$$\frac{dv}{dz} = h(u, v), \qquad v(x) = c, \qquad 0 < z < x. \tag{15.1}$$

Here $v(z)$ represents the flux to the left at an intermediate point z, and $u(z)$ represents the corresponding flux to the right, in the steady-state condition. The two-point boundary condition in (15.1) arises quite naturally from the physical fact that we assume a constant flux per unit time of intensity c incident at $z = x$ and no flux per unit time incident at $z = 0$, as indicated in Fig. 2.

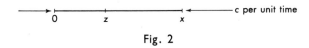

Fig. 2

The function $u(x)$ represents the reflected flux, a quantity that we wish to study as a function of the length, x.

Let u_1, v_1 be the solutions of the corresponding equations for thickness $x + \Delta$,

$$\frac{du_1}{dz} = g(u_1, v_1), \qquad u_1(0) = 0,$$

$$\frac{dv_1}{dz} = h(u_1, v_1), \qquad v_1(x + \Delta) = c, \qquad 0 < z < x + \Delta, \tag{15.2}$$

where Δ is an infinitesimal. This set of equations can be converted into one with the new boundary conditions

$$v_1(x) + \Delta v_1'(x) = c = v_1(x) + \Delta h(u_1(x), v_1(x))$$
$$= v_1(x) + \Delta h(u(x), v(x)) + 0(\Delta), \tag{15.3}$$

or, finally,

$$v_1(x) = c - \Delta h(u(x), v(x)) + 0(\Delta), \tag{15.4}$$

since $u_1 = u + 0(\Delta)$, $v_1 = v + 0(\Delta)$.

Now that we have both sets of equations over the same interval $0 < z < x$, let us write

$$u_1 = u + w\Delta, \qquad v_1 = v + q\Delta, \tag{15.5}$$

where w and q are functions of z. Then, proceeding in the usual way, we obtain the linear perturbation equations

$$\frac{dw}{dz} = wg_u + qg_v , \qquad w(0) = 0,$$

$$\frac{dq}{dz} = wh_u + qh_v , \qquad q(x) = - h(u(x), v(x)). \tag{15.6}$$

Returning to (15.1), let us examine the dependence of the solutions upon c (the intensity of incident flux). Taking partial derivatives with respect to c, we have

$$\frac{d}{dz}(u_c) = u_c g_u + v_c g_v , \qquad u_c(0) = 0,$$

$$\frac{d}{dz}(v_c) = u_c h_u + v_c h_v , \qquad v_c(x) = 1 \tag{15.7}$$

(compare to Exercise 14.1). Assuming that this linear system possesses a unique solution (as is readily established rigorously for small x), we see that the solution of the system in (15.6) can be written in terms of the solution of (15.7),

$$w = - h(u(x), v(x)) u_c ,$$

$$q = - h(u(x), v(x)) v_c . \tag{15.8}$$

Since

$$u_1(x + \Delta) = u_1(x) + \Delta u_1'(x) = u_1(x) + \Delta g(u, v) + 0(\Delta)$$

$$= (u(x) + \Delta w) + \Delta g(u, v) + 0(\Delta), \tag{15.9}$$

upon setting $u(x) = r(x, c)$, we see that r satisfies the equation

$$r(x + \Delta, c) = r(x, c) + \Delta w + \Delta g + 0(\Delta), \tag{15.10}$$

or

$$\frac{\partial r}{\partial x} = - h(r, c) \frac{\partial r}{\partial c} + g(r, c), \qquad r(0, c) = 0. \tag{15.11}$$

This equation illustrates the relation between the change in the reflected flux as the length of the rod changes, and as the intensity changes. As mentioned above, this relation can be derived directly using invariant imbedding techniques.

COMMENTS AND BIBLIOGRAPHY

See the following papers:

R. Bellman and R. Kalaba, "On the Principle of Invariant Imbedding and Propagation through Inhomogeneous Media," *Proc. Nat. Acad. Sci. US,* **42**, 629-632, 1956.

―― and ――, "Random Walk, Scattering and Invariant Imbedding― I: One-dimensional Case," *Proc. Nat. Acad. Sci. US,* **43**, 930-933, 1957.

――, ――, and G. M. Wing, "On the Principle of Invariant Imbedding and One-dimensional Neutron Multiplication," *Proc. Nat. Acad. Sci. US,* **43**, 517-520, 1957.

――, ――, and ――, "On the Principle of Invariant Imbedding and Neutron Transport Theory―I: One-dimensional Case," *J. Math. and Mech.,* **7**, 149-162, 1958.

――, ――, and ――, "Invariant Imbedding and Variational Principles in Transport Theory," *Bull. Am. Math. Soc.,* **67**, 396-399, 1961.

For an application of dynamic programming to the study of problems of this nature, see

R. Bellman, "Functional Equations in the Theory of Dynamic Programming― VIII: The Variation of Green's Functions for the One-dimensional Case," *Proc. Nat. Acad. Sci. US,* **43**, 839-841, 1957.

―― and R. S. Lehman, "Functional Equations in the Theory of Dynamic Programming―IX: Variational Analysis, Analytic Continuation, and Imbedding of Operators," *Proc. Nat. Acad. Sci. US,* **44**, 905-907, 1958.

―― and ――, "Functional Equations in the Theory of Dynamic Programming―X: Resolvents, Characteristic Functions and Values," *Duke Math. J.,* **27**, 55-70, 1960.

For an application of dynamic programming to more general two-point boundary-value problems, see Section **12** of Chapter 2.

EXERCISES

15.1. Consider the equations

$$u' = av, \qquad v' = -au, \qquad a > 0,$$

with the two-point conditions

$$u(0) = 0, \qquad v(x) = y.$$

Show that the solution is

$$u = \frac{y \sin az}{\cos ax}, \qquad v = \frac{y \cos az}{\cos ax}$$

for $0 \leq x < \pi/2a$, and that $x = \pi/2a$ is a *critical length* at which reflected and transmitted fluxes become infinite.

15.2. Consider the equations $u' = v - buv$, $v' = -u + buv$, $b > 0$, $u(0) = 0$, $v(x) = y$, obtained by introducing an interaction between fluxes in different directions, and normalizing lengths so that $a = 1$. Show that

$$0 \leq u(z) \leq b^{-1},$$

for *all* $z \geq 0$. Thus, there is no critical length.

15.3. What happens if we try to solve for small b by use of the usual perturbation equations

$$u = u_0 + bu_1 + b^2 u_2 + \cdots,$$
$$v = v_0 + bv_1 + b^2 v_2 + \cdots.$$

(For these results and further discussion, see, R. Bellman, R. Kalaba, and G. M. Wing, "Invariant Imbedding and Neutron Transport Theory—III: Neutron-neutron Collision Processes," *J. Math. and Mech.*, **8**, 249-262, 1959.)

16. Multidimensional Considerations

To handle differential equations of order higher than two in any elegant and satisfying fashion, it is imperative to use some rudimentary vector-matrix analysis. Before embarking upon this, let us provide some motivation.

Consider the nth order linear differential equation

$$\frac{d^n u}{dt^n} + a_1(t) \frac{d^{n-1}u}{dt^{n-1}} + a_2(t) \frac{d^{n-2}u}{dt^{n-2}} + \cdots + a_n(t) u = 0. \tag{16.1}$$

Introduce the functions

$$x_1 = u,$$
$$x_2 = \frac{du}{dt},$$
$$\vdots$$
$$x_n = \frac{d^{n-1}u}{dt^{n-1}}. \tag{16.2}$$

Then (16.1) takes the form

$$\frac{dx_n}{dt} + a_1(t)\, x_n + a_2(t)\, x_{n-1} + \cdots + a_n(t)\, x_1 = 0. \tag{16.3}$$

Hence, combining (16.2) and (16.3) we have a system of first order equations

$$\frac{dx_1}{dt} = x_2 ,$$

$$\frac{dx_2}{dt} = x_3 ,$$

$$\vdots$$

$$\frac{dx_n}{dt} = - a_1(t)\, x_n - a_2(t)\, x_{n-1} - \cdots - a_n(t)\, x_1. \tag{16.4}$$

Introducing the vector x and the matrix $A(t)$,

$$x = \begin{pmatrix} x_1 \\ x_2 \\ \vdots \\ x_n \end{pmatrix}, \quad A(t) = \begin{pmatrix} 0 & 1 & 0 & \cdots \\ 0 & 0 & 1 & \cdots \\ \vdots & & \vdots & \\ - a_n(t) & - a_{n-1}(t) & \cdots & - a_1(t) \end{pmatrix}, \tag{16.5}$$

we may write (16.4) in the form

$$\frac{dx}{dt} = A(t)\, x. \tag{16.6}$$

A perturbed system will have the form

$$\frac{dx}{dt} = (A(t) + \epsilon B(t))\, x. \tag{16.7}$$

We now face the problem of writing the solution of the perturbed equation in terms of the solution of the original equation. As usual, let us begin with the case of constant coefficients, where some particularly elegant results and methods exist.

17. The Matrix Exponential

Given the vector differential equation

$$\frac{dx}{dt} = Ax, \quad x(0) = c, \tag{17.1}$$

where x and c are n-dimensional vectors and A is an $n \times n$ matrix with constant elements, we would like to write the solution in the form

$$x = e^{At}c. \tag{17.2}$$

To validate this useful and intuitive representation, let us introduce the matrix function

$$F(A, t) = I + At + \frac{A^2t^2}{2!} + \cdots + \frac{A^nt^n}{n!} + \cdots. \tag{17.3}$$

As in the one-dimensional case, it is easy to establish the fact that the series converges uniformly in any finite portion of the complex t plane, for fixed A, and thus represents an entire analytic matrix function of t.

We can thus differentiate term by term and obtain the relation

$$\frac{dF}{dt} = A \left(I + At + \frac{A^2t^2}{2!} + \cdots \right) = AF, \tag{17.4}$$

with the obvious initial value $F(A, 0) = I$. Since e^{At} has no intrinsic meaning for A a matrix, there is no harm done in using this symbol to denote the function $F(A, t)$, and there are some advantages. As we shall see, e^{At} has some of the properties of the scalar exponential, but not all.

EXERCISES

17.1. Prove that the vector $e^{At}c$ satisfies the equation of (17.1).

17.2. Prove that $e^{A(t+s)} = e^{At}e^{As}$ for all t and s, and thus that $(e^{At})^{-1} = e^{-At}$.

17.3. Prove that $e^{(A+B)t} = e^{At}e^{Bt}$ for all t if and only if $AB = BA$.

17.4. Consider the system of differential equations $dy_i/dt = g_i(y_1, y_2, \cdots, y_N)$, $i = 1, 2, \cdots, N$, $y_i(0) = c_i$. Let $f(y_1, y_2, \cdots, y_N)$ be a function of the solution. Show that f satisfies the *linear* partial differential equation

$$\frac{\partial f}{\partial t} = \sum_{i=1}^{N} \frac{\partial f}{\partial y_i} g_i(y_1, y_2, \cdots, y_N).$$

17.5. Hence, show that f has the symbolic form

$$f(y) = \exp\left(t \sum_{i=1}^{N} g_i(c_1, c_2, \cdots, c_N) \frac{\partial}{\partial c_i} \right) f(c_1, c_2, \cdots, c_N),$$

a power series expansion in t. (See: W. Gröbner, *Die Lie-Reihen und ihre Anwendungen*, Berlin: VEB Deutscher Verlag der Wissenschaften, 1960, and, ———

and F. Cap, *A New Method to Solve Differential Equations: Lie Series and their Applications in Physics and Engineering*, Washington, D. C.: Research Contract N 62558-2992, U. S. European Research Contracts Program, Naval Research Office.

See also

I. Fredholm, "Sur la réduction de la Mécanique rationnelle à une équation intégrale linéaire," *C. R.*, **171**, 426-428, 1920.

COMMENTS AND BIBLIOGRAPHY

One of the great challenges of modern physics is that of obtaining useful approximate relations for $e^{(A+\epsilon B)t}$ in the case where $AB \neq BA$. For the requisite background in matrix theory and many further results, see

R. Bellman, *Introduction to Matrix Analysis*, New York: McGraw-Hill Book Co., Inc., 1960.

For a generalization of exponential series, see F. V. Atkinson, "Some aspects of Baxter's functional equation," *J. Math. Analysis and Appl.*, to appear.

18. $e^{A+\epsilon B}$

To obtain a perturbation expansion of $e^{A+\epsilon B}$ in powers of ϵ, following the line of the preceding section, we regard it as the solution of the linear matrix differential equation

$$X'(t) = (A + \epsilon B) X(t), \qquad X(0) = I, \tag{18.1}$$

evaluated at the point $t = 1$. Writing this in the form

$$X'(t) - AX(t) = \epsilon BX(t), \qquad X(0) = I, \tag{18.2}$$

and using the integrating factor e^{-At}, we readily obtain the equivalent linear integral equation

$$X(t) = e^{At} + \epsilon \int_0^t e^{A(t-s)} BX(s) \, ds. \tag{18.3}$$

Iterating, we obtain the perturbation expansion

$$X(t) = e^{At} + \epsilon \int_0^t e^{A(t-s)} Be^{As} \, ds + 0(\epsilon^2). \tag{18.4}$$

Hence, we obtain the rather surprising result

$$e^{(A+\epsilon B)} = e^A + \epsilon \int_0^1 e^{A(1-s)} \, Be^{As} \, ds + 0(\epsilon^2). \qquad (18.5)$$

EXERCISES

18.1. Write

$$\operatorname{tr}(X) = \sum_{i=1}^n x_{ii} \, ,$$

for an arbitrary matrix $X = (x_{ij})$. Show that

$$\operatorname{tr}\left(e^{A+\epsilon B}\right) = \operatorname{tr}\left(e^A\right) + \epsilon \operatorname{tr}\left(e^A B\right) + 0(\epsilon^2).$$

18.2. What is the coefficient of ϵ^2 in the series expansion of $e^{A+\epsilon B}$?

18.3. Write the equation $u'' + (1 + f(t)) \, u = 0$ in the form

$$u' = v, \qquad v' = -(1 + f(t)) \, u,$$

and thus obtain an integral equation for the vector whose components are u and v.

18.4. Show that the solution of

$$\frac{dX}{dt} = AX + XB, \qquad X(0) = C.$$

is given by $X = e^{At} C e^{Bt}$, and thus obtain a solution of $AY + YB = -C$.

18.5. Obtain the constant matrices C_2 and C_3 determined by the expansion

$$e^{(A+B)t} = e^{At} e^{Bt} e^{C_2 t^2} e^{C_3 t^3} \cdots$$

in the following fashion. Write the differential equation for $e^{(A+B)t}$, $dX/dt = (A + B) \, X$, $X(0) = I$, and set $X = e^{At} Y$, and $Y = e^{Bt} W$. The result is

$$\frac{dW}{dt} = (e^{-Bt} e^{-At} Be^{At} e^{Bt} - B) \, W.$$

Show that

$$e^{-Bt} e^{-At} \, Be^{At} \, e^{Bt} - B = (BA - AB) \, t + 0(t^2),$$

and thus that $C_2 = (BA - AB)/2$.

Determine C_3 in this way and obtain a general recurrence relation.

COMMENTS AND BIBLIOGRAPHY

For a different approach to perturbation series based upon operator ordering, see

R. P. Feynman, "An Operator Calculus Having Applications in Quantum Electrodynamics," *Phys. Rev.*, **84**, 108-128, 1951.

Some other important references are

K. Chen, "Decomposition of Differential Equations," *Math. Annalen*, **146**, 263-278, 1962.

T. F. Jordan and E. C. G. Sudarshan, "Lie Group Dynamical Formalism and the Relation between Quantum Mechanics and Classical Mechanics," *Rev. of Mod. Phys.*, 33, 515-524, 1961.

Lowdin Per-Olov, "Studies in Perturbation Theory, IV, Solution of Eigenvalue Problem by Projection Operator Formalism," *J. Math. and Phys.*, 3, 969-982, 1962.

W. Magnus, "On the Exponential Solution of Differential Equations for a Linear Operator," *Comm. Pure Appl. Math.*, 7, 649-673, 1954.

F. J. Murray, "Perturbation Theory and Lie Algebra," *J. Math. and Phys.*, 3, 451-468, 1962.

G. H. Weiss and A. A. Maradudin, "The Baker-Hausdorff Formula and a Problem in Crystal Physics," *J. Math. and Phys.*, 3, 771-777, 1962.

Further references will be found there and in

R. Bellman, *Introduction to Matrix Analysis*, New York: McGraw-Hill Book Co., Inc., 1960.

19. Variable Coefficients

Very much the same technique permits us to obtain a perturbation expansion of the solution of

$$\frac{dx}{dt} = (A(t) + \epsilon B(t))\, x. \tag{19.1}$$

We write it as

$$\frac{dx}{dt} - A(t)\, x = \epsilon B(t)\, x, \tag{19.2}$$

and convert it into the integral equation

$$x = Y(t)\, c + \epsilon \int_0^t Y(t)\, Y(s)^{-1}\, B(s)\, x(s)\, ds, \tag{19.3}$$

where $Y(t)$ is the solution of the matrix equation

$$\frac{dY}{dt} = A(t)\,Y, \qquad Y(0) = I. \tag{19.4}$$

Iteration yields the result

$$x = Y(t)\,c + \epsilon \left(\int_0^t Y(t)\,Y(s)^{-1}\,B(s)\,Y(s)\,ds \right) c + 0(\epsilon^2). \tag{19.5}$$

EXERCISES

1. Solve the equation $dx/dt - A(t)\,x = y$ by means of the variation of parameters technique, putting $x = Y(t)\,w$.

COMMENTS AND BIBLIOGRAPHY

For the case of general linear functional equations, the foregoing method must be replaced by the method of the adjoint. See

R. Bellman and K. L. Cooke, "Asymptotic Behavior of Solutions of Differential-difference Equations," *Memoirs of Am. Math. Soc.*, No. 35, 1959.

20. Baker-Campbell-Hausdorff Series

Occasionally, we wish to proceed in the other direction and write $e^A e^B$ in the form e^C. A general theorem in matrix algebra tells us that this is always possible, but the determination of C is nontrivial. If $AB = BA$, then $C = A + B$. If $AB \neq BA$, the problem is more interesting.

It is not difficult to show that

$$C = A + B + \tfrac{1}{2}(AB - BA) + \cdots, \tag{20.1}$$

using the relation

$$C = \log\left(e^A e^B\right) = \log\left(I + e^A e^B - I\right)$$

$$= (e^A e^B - I) - \frac{(e^A e^B - I)^2}{2} + \cdots, \tag{20.2}$$

and so on.

EXERCISES

20.1. If $AB - BA = I$ and c_1, c_2 are scalars, then

$$e^{c_1 A + c_2 B} = e^{c_1 A} e^{c_2 B} e^{c_1 c_2 / 2}.$$

(R. A. Sack, "Taylor's Theorem for shift Operators," *Phil. Mag.*, **3**, 497-503, 1958.)

COMMENTS AND BIBLIOGRAPHY

H. F. Baker, "On the Integration of Linear Differential Equations," *Proc. London. Math. Soc.*, **34**, 347-360, 1902; **35**, 333-374, 1903; second series, **2**, 293-296, 1904.

————, "Alternants and Continuous Groups," *Proc. London Math. Soc.*, second series, **3**, 24-27, 1904.

W. Magnus, "Algebraic Aspects of the Theory of Systems of Linear Differential Equations," *Com. Pure Appl. Math.*, **7**, No. 4, 1954.

Further references will be found in

R. Bellman, *Introduction to Matrix Analysis*, New York: McGraw-Hill Book Company, Inc., 1960.

21. Nonlinear Perturbation

Up to now, we have considered *linear* vector equations of the form

$$\frac{dx}{dt} = A(t)\, x, \quad x(0) = c, \tag{21.1}$$

and the effect of changes in the coefficients, and *nonlinear* equations as far as changes in the initial values and interval of interest was concerned. We now wish to study the effect of adding a nonlinear term to the foregoing equation. The new equation has the form

$$\frac{dx}{dt} = A(t)\, x + h(x), \quad x(0) = c. \tag{21.2}$$

We shall constrain our attention to the case where $A(t)$ is constant.

To motivate a discussion of equations of this complex type, let us consider a system of differential equations of the form

$$\frac{dx_i}{dt} = g_i(x_1, x_2, \cdots, x_N), \qquad x_i(0) = c_i, \qquad i = 1, 2, \cdots, N, \qquad (21.3)$$

($dx/dt = g(x)$ in vector notation), where each function g_i is an analytic function of the x_i in the neighborhood of the point $v_i = a_i$, $i = 1, 2, \cdots, N$, an *equilibrium point* defined as the solution of the simultaneous equations

$$g_i(a_1, a_2, \cdots, a_N) = 0. \qquad (21.4)$$

In many engineering and physical situations, these represent positions of equilibrium of systems in phase space.

To determine whether or not these equilibrium points are stable or not, we proceed as follows. Set $v_i = a_i + y_i$ and expand the right-hand sides of (21.3) about the point $a = (a_1, a_2, \cdots, a_N)$. The resulting equations are

$$\frac{dy_i}{dt} = g_i(a_1 + y_1, a_2 + y_2, \cdots, a_N + y_N)$$

$$= g_i(a_1, a_2, \cdots, a_N) + \sum_{j=1}^{N} a_{ij} y_j + \text{higher order terms in the } y_i. \qquad (21.5)$$

The constant coefficients a_{ij} are obtained from the partial derivatives $\partial g_{ij} \partial y_j$, evaluated at the point a.

It is natural to expect that there will be connections between the behavior of the solutions of the *linear* system

$$\frac{dz_i}{dt} = \sum_{j=1}^{N} a_{ij} z_j, \qquad (21.6)$$

and those of the original nonlinear equation, in the neighborhood of the origin, $y_i = z_i = 0$, $i = 1, 2, \cdots, N$. This is indeed the case, but the full story is not a simple one.

A fundamental result of Poincaré and Lyapunov asserts this equivalence in one simple, but very important, case, namely where *all* solutions of the linear system in (21.6) go to zero as $t \to \infty$.

EXERCISES

21.1. Show that all solutions of $dx/dt = Ax$ go to zero as $t \to \infty$ if, and only if, all of the characteristic roots of A have negative real parts.

21.2. Consider the scalar equation

$$\frac{du}{dt} = u(1 - u), \qquad u(0) = c.$$

Show that if $c < 0$, $u(t) \to 0$ as $t \to \infty$; if $c > 0$, $u \to 1$ as $t \to \infty$.

21.3. Consider the equation

$$u' = -u + u^3, \qquad u(0) = c.$$

The change of variable $u = cv$ converts this into the equation

$$v' = -v + c^2 v^3, \qquad v(0) = 1.$$

Hence, the study of nonlinear equations with small initial values is equivalent to the study of nonlinear equations with arbitrary initial values and small nonlinear terms.

22. Poincaré-Lyapunov Theorem

Let us now state the fundamental result in the study of the stability of equilibrium points.

THEOREM.   If

(a) all solutions of the linear system $dx/dt = Ax$, approach the origin as $t \to \infty$,

(b) the initial value, c, is sufficiently close to the origin,

(c) the nonlinear term, $g(x)$, consists of a vector all of whose components are power series lacking constant and linear terms,

then the solution of

$$\frac{dy}{dt} = Ay + g(y), \qquad y(0) = c, \tag{22.2}$$

approaches the origin as $t \to \infty$.

This result furnishes a simple sufficient condition for the stability of an equilibrium point. If condition (a) is not satisfied, perturbations of some type (that is, some values of c) may be stable, but there will always exist others that are not. There are really two types of behavior to consider, that where the system returns eventually to its original state, and that where its deviation from the initial state remains uniformly bounded over time. The over-all problem of determining the behavior of the solutions of (22.2) in the case where all of the characteristic roots of (22.2) have nonpositive real parts is quite complex as the reader will see upon consulting the references below.

COMMENTS AND BIBLIOGRAPHY

The foregoing result is not difficult to establish, and there are many simple proofs extant, stemming from the original research of Poincaré and Lyapunov, and the subsequent work of Perron, Hukuhara and others. For this material, extensions and other results pertaining to stability, see

R. Bellman, *Stability Theory of Differential Equations*, New York: McGraw-Hill Book Co., Inc., 1954.

S. Lefschetz, *Differential Equations: Geometric Theory*, New York: Interscience Publishers, Inc., 1957.

L. Cesari, *Asymptotic Behavior and Stability Problems in Ordinary Differential Equations*, Berlin: Springer-Verlag, 1959.

A very flexible and powerful method for the treatment of stability in the large and for the study of general functional equations is the "second method" of Lyapunov. See

L. P. LaSalle and S. Lefschetz, *Stability by Lyapunov's Direct Method with Applications*, New York: Academic Press Inc., 1961.

N. Letov, *Stability in Nonlinear Control Systems*, Princeton, N. J.: Princeton University Press, 1961.

V. V. Nemytskii and V. V. Stepanov, *Qualitative Theory of Differential Equations*, Princeton, N. J.: Princeton University Press, 1960.

Corresponding results exist for other types of functional equations such as differential-difference equations and parabolic partial differential equations; see

R. Bellman and K. L. Cooke, *Differential-difference Equations*, New York: Academic Press Inc., 1962.

C. Olech, "A Connection between Two Certain Methods of Successive Approximation in Differential Equations," Polska Akademia Nauk. Instytut Matematyczny. *Annales polonici mathematici*, **11**, No. 3, 238-245, 1962.

23. Asymptotic Behavior

Having obtained sufficient conditions for asymptotic stability of solutions of

$$\frac{dx}{dt} = Ax + g(x), \tag{23.1}$$

we now wish to ascertain how rapidly the solution tends to zero. To illustrate the type of investigation we have in mind, consider the scalar equation

$$\frac{du}{dt} = -u + u^2, \qquad u(0) = c. \tag{23.2}$$

We can, of course, use the explicit analytic solution to determine all properties of interest. Since, however, this approach is not available in dealing with the general vector equation, let us develop another route.

Considering u^2 as a forcing term, we can convert (23.1) into the nonlinear integral equation

$$u = ce^{-t} + \int_0^t e^{-(t-s)} u^2(s) \, ds. \tag{23.3}$$

One proof of the Poincaré-Lyapunov theorem proceeds along these lines. Setting $u = e^{-t}v$, we have

$$v = c + \int_0^t e^{-s} v^2(s) \, ds. \tag{23.4}$$

It is now easy to prove in a number of ways that $| v(t) | \leq 2 | c |$ for all $t \geq 0$ provided that $| c |$ is sufficiently small. Using this bound in the integral, we see that it converges. Hence, as $t \to \infty$,

$$v \sim c + \int_0^\infty e^{-s} v^2(s) \, ds, \tag{23.5}$$

a function of c. To obtain a more revealing representation, we return to (25.4) and iterate,

$$v = c + \int_0^t e^{-s} \left[c + \int_0^s e^{-s_1} v^2(s_1) \, ds_1 \right]^2 ds$$

$$= c + c^2 \int_0^t e^{-s} \, ds + 0(c^3). \tag{23.6}$$

Continuing in this way, we can obtain all the terms in the power series expansion of $v(\infty)$ as a function of c. This is a rather difficult and tedious process. Can we develop a simpler approach?

24. Functional Equations

Let us treat the more general equation

$$\frac{du}{dt} = -u + g(u), \qquad u(0) = c, \tag{24.1}$$

where $g(u) = a_2 u^2 + a_3 u^3 + \cdots$ for $| u |$ sufficiently small. By virtue of the Poincaré-Lyapunov theorem, and its immediate extension, we, as above, are assured of the existence of the function $f(c)$ defined by

$$f(c) = \lim_{t \to \infty} ue^t. \tag{24.2}$$

To derive an equation for $f(c)$, we write

$$f(c) = \lim_{t\to\infty} [u(t)\, e^t] = \lim_{t\to\infty} [u(t + \varDelta)\, e^{t+\varDelta}]$$

$$= e^{\varDelta} \lim_{t\to\infty} [u(t + \varDelta)\, e^t] = e^{\varDelta} f(u(\varDelta)), \tag{24.3}$$

since $u(t + \varDelta)$ is the solution of the differential equation in (24.1) that has the initial value $u(\varDelta)$. Since

$$u(\varDelta) = c + (g(c) - c)\,\varDelta + o(\varDelta),$$

(24.3) yields

$$f(c) = (1 + \varDelta) f(c + (g(c) - c)\,\varDelta) + o(\varDelta)$$
$$= f(c) + \varDelta f(c) + (g(c) - c) f'(c)\,\varDelta + o(\varDelta), \tag{24.4}$$

or, in the limit as $\varDelta \to 0$,

$$(g(c) - c) f'(c) + f(c) = 0. \tag{24.5}$$

It is now easy to determine the coefficients in the power series expansion of $f(c)$. Writing

$$f(c) = c + \sum_{k=2}^{\infty} b_k c^k,$$

$$g(c) = \sum_{k=2}^{\infty} a_k c^k, \tag{24.6}$$

we obtain from (24.5) the recurrence relation

$$b_N = -\, N b_{N-1} + \sum_{\substack{r+s=N \\ 2 \le r \le N}} s b_s a_r, \qquad N \ge 2. \tag{24.7}$$

EXERCISES

24.1. Obtain the foregoing result directly from the explicit solution of

$$u' = -\,u + g(u), \qquad u(0) = c.$$

COMMENTS AND BIBLIOGRAPHY

There is no difficulty in extending this technique in a straightforward way to handle the corresponding problem for systems of nonlinear differential equations and for more general classes of functional equations. See, for example,

R. Bellman and J. M. Richardson, "On the Asymptotic Behavior of Solutions of Nonlinear Differential Equations," *J. Math. Analysis and Appl.*, **4**, 470-474, 1962.

25. Relative Invariants

Let us now sketch a method that yields a great deal more information in dealing with analytic differential equations. Consider the scalar equation

$$\frac{du}{dt} = a_1 u + a_2 u^2 + \cdots, \qquad u(0) = c, \tag{25.1}$$

where $a_1 \neq 0$. Let us see if we can determine a function of the solution u, $f(u)$, possessing the property that

$$\frac{df}{dt} = \lambda f. \tag{25.2}$$

Taking f to have the form

$$f(u) = u + b_2 u^2 + \cdots, \tag{25.3}$$

we obtain, upon combining (25.2) and (25.1),

$$\begin{aligned}
\frac{df}{dt} &= (1 + 2b_2 u + \cdots)\frac{du}{dt} \\
&= (1 + 2b_2 u + \cdots)(a_1 u + a_2 u^2 + \cdots) \\
&= \lambda(u + b_2 u^2 + \cdots).
\end{aligned} \tag{25.4}$$

Equating coefficients of a, we see that $\lambda = a_1$, and that we can obtain a simple recurrence relation for the coefficients b_n.

Having thus determined $f(u)$, we return to (25.2) and note that we can solve explicitly,

$$f(u) = e^{\lambda t} f(c) \qquad \text{(since } u(0) = c\text{).} \tag{25.5}$$

Thus u itself is given by

$$u = f^{-1}(e^{\lambda t} f(c)). \tag{25.6}$$

If Re $(\lambda) < 0$, this yields the asymptotic behavior of u as $t \to \infty$. The same technique can be applied to the study of vector differential equations with the usual complications of multidimensionality. We shall sketch the results in the exercises that follow.

EXERCISES

25.1. Consider the two-dimensional system $dx/dt = Ax + g(x)$, $x(0) = c$, where A has distinct characteristic roots and $g(x)$ is analytic in the components of x, lacking zero order and first order terms. Show that we can make a change of variable $x = Ty$ that has the effect of converting it into a system of the form

$$\frac{dy_1}{dt} = \lambda_1 y_1 + h_1(y_1, y_2), \qquad y_1(0) = c_1,$$

$$\frac{dy_2}{dt} = \lambda_2 y_2 + h_2(y_1, y_2), \qquad y_2(0) = c_2,$$

where h_1 and h_2 are of second order or higher.

25.2. Let f be a scalar function of z_1 and z_2 determined by the condition that

$$f = z_1 + f_2 + f_3 + \cdots + f_n + \cdots,$$

where f_n is a homogeneous polynomial of degree n and $df/dt = \lambda f$. Show that $\lambda = \lambda_1$ and that we obtain a linear partial differential equation for f_n in terms of $f_2, f_3, \cdots, f_{n-1}$.

25.3. Write

$$f_2 = u z_1^2 + 2v z_1 z_2 + w z_2^2,$$

where u, v, w are constants to be determined. Show that u, v, w satisfy a system of linear algebraic equations of the form

$$2\lambda_1 u + \lambda_1 u = a_1,$$
$$(\lambda_1 + \lambda_2) v + \lambda_1 v = a_2,$$
$$2\lambda_2 w + \lambda_1 w = a_3.$$

Hence, u, v, and w can be determined if $\lambda_1 \neq 0$, $2\lambda_1 + \lambda_2 \neq 0$, $\lambda_1 + 2\lambda_2 \neq 0$.

25.4. Show, similarly, that the function f_n is uniquely determined for each n if no relation of the type $r\lambda_1 + s\lambda_2 \neq 0$, where r and s are positive integers.

COMMENTS AND BIBLIOGRAPHY

Results of the foregoing nature are intimately connected with work in the classical theory of analytic differential equations done by Poincaré, G. D. Birkhoff, Lyapunov, and others. See, for example,

A. M. Liapunov, "Problème général de la stabilité du mouvement," *Annals of Math.* Studies No. 17, Princeton, N. J.: Princeton Univ. Press, 1947.

W. Wasow, "Studies of Nonlinear Differential Equations with a Parameter by Asymptotic Series," *Ann. of Math.*, **69**, No. 2, 486-509, 1959.

G. D. Birkhoff, "Dynamical Systems," *Am. Math. Soc.*, Vol. **IV**, 1927.

The linear systems obtained in determining the coefficients of f_n are connected with Kronecker products and sums; see

R. Bellman, *Introduction to Matrix Analysis*, New York: McGraw-Hill Book Co., Inc., 1960.

For further details concerning the foregoing method, see

R. Bellman, "Formal Solutions of Analytic Differential Equations," *Bolletino d'Unione Matematico*, 1962.

26. Iteration and Recurrence Relations

An analogue of the nonlinear differential equation treated in Section 25 and earlier sections is the nonlinear difference equation

$$u_{n+1} = a_1 u_n + a_2 u_n^2 + \cdots, \qquad u_0 = c. \tag{26.1}$$

Writing

$$g(u) = a_1 u + a_2 u^2 + \cdots, \tag{26.2}$$

we see that the determination of u_n, using (26.1), is equivalent to obtaining the nth iterate of the function $g(u)$, namely

$$u_1 = g(c),$$
$$u_2 = g(g(c)), \tag{26.3}$$

and so on.

Considering the vector analogue of (26.1),

$$x_{n+1} = A x_n + g(x_n), \qquad x(0) = c, \tag{26.4}$$

it is easy to obtain the analogue of the Poincaré-Lyapunov theorem, to wit

THEOREM.   If

      (a) all characteristic roots of A are less than one in absolute value,

      (b) $\| c \|$ is sufficiently small,

      (c) all components of $g(x)$ are power series in the components of x lacking constant and first order terms,   (26.5)

then $x_n \to 0$ as $n \to \infty$.

To determine the asymptotic behavior more accurately, we shall discuss an analogue of the results of the previous section.

EXERCISES

26.1. Given the recurrence relation

$$u_{n+1} = \frac{au_n + b}{cu_n + d}, \qquad u_0 = c,$$

determine the possible asymptotic forms of u_n as $n \to \infty$.

26.2. Consider the same problem for the matrix relation

$$X_{n+1} = (AX_n + B)(CX_n + D)^{-1}.$$

COMMENTS AND BIBLIOGRAPHY

A proof of the foregoing result together with additional references will be found in

R. Bellman, "On the Boundedness of Solutions of Nonlinear Differential and Difference Equations," *Trans. Am. Math. Soc.*, **62**, 357-386, 1947.

The original result is due to Perron.

27. The Abel-Schröder Functional Equation

Returning to the recurrence relation

$$u_{n+1} = a_1 u_n + a_2 u_n^2 + \cdots,$$

$$= g(u_n), \qquad u_0 = c, \tag{27.1}$$

let us assume that $0 < |a_1| < 1$. Then, as $n \to \infty$,

$$u_n \sim a_1^n f(c). \tag{27.2}$$

This function $f(c)$ satisfies the following important equation

$$f(c) = \lim_{n \to \infty} \frac{u_n(c)}{a_1^n} = \lim_{n \to \infty} \frac{u_{n+1}(c)}{a_1^{n+1}}$$

$$= \lim_{n \to \infty} \frac{u_n(g(c))}{a_1^{n+1}} = \frac{f(g(c))}{a_1}. \tag{27.3}$$

If we normalize $f(c)$ by the requirement that

$$f(c) = c + b_2 c^2 + \cdots, \tag{27.4}$$

we can determine the coefficients b_2, b_3, $\cdots$, from the foregoing functional equation by direct equating of coefficients. Having determined $f(c)$, the asymptotic behavior of u_n is immediate from (27.2).

EXERCISES

27.1. Determine $f(c)$ in the case where

$$g(c) = \frac{a_1 c}{1 + a_2 c} \, .$$

27.2. Determine the recurrence relations for the coefficients in $f(c)$ when

$$g(c) = a_1 c + a_2 c^2.$$

27.3. What are the results corresponding to those given above, when

$$a_1 = a_2 = \cdots = a_k = 0, \qquad 0 < |a_{k+1}| < 1 ?$$

27.4. Show that every power series of the form

$$g(c) = a_1 c + a_2 c^2 + \cdots, \qquad |a_1| < 1,$$

can be considered to be the value at $t = 1$ of the solution of an analytic differential equation of the form

$$\frac{du}{dt} = b_1 u + b_2 u^2 + \cdots, \qquad u(0) = c,$$

with Re $(b_1) < 0$.

COMMENTS AND BIBLIOGRAPHY

An enormous amount of work has been done in the field of iteration, and the foregoing results due to Schröder have been extensively developed and generalized to the multidimensional case. Further references and discussion may be found in

R. Bellman, "The Iteration of Power Series in Two Variables," *Duke Math. J.*, **19**, 339-347, 1952.

J. Hadamard, "Two Works in Iteration and Related Questions," *Bull. Am. Math. Soc.* **50**, 67-75, 1944.

A. A. Sarsanov, "Analytic Iteration of Functions of Two Variables," *Soviet Math.*, **3**, No. 2, 452-455, 1962.

H. Töpfer, "Komplexe Iterationsindizes ganzer und rationaler Funktionen," *Math. Annalen*, **121**, 191-222, 1949-1950.

M. Urabe, "Equations of Schröder," *J. of Sci. Hiroshima Univ.*, Series A, **15**, 113-131, 203-233, 1951.

Interest in iteration revived in connection with the development of a theory of biological mutation and of neutron transport, particular examples of a general theory of branching processes created by T. E. Harris, and others; see

T. E. Harris, *Branching Processes*, Springer, Berlin: Ergebnisse der Math., to appear in 1963.

Another mainstream of mathematics having its source in the work discussed above is the theory of semigroups; see

E. Hille, "Functional Analysis and Semi-groups," *Am. Math. Soc. Colloq. Publ.*, **31**, 1948.

28. Irregular Perturbation

So far we have studied perturbation problems involving equations having the form

$$x' = Ax + \epsilon g(x), \qquad x(0) = c, \qquad (28.1)$$

where $g(x)$ may be linear or nonlinear. Questions of much greater intricacy arise when the equation has the form

$$\epsilon x' = Ax + g(x), \qquad (28.2)$$

or

$$x' = Ax + \epsilon g(x, x', x''). \qquad (28.3)$$

In other words, we can expect difficulties when the equation obtained by setting $\epsilon = 0$ is of lower order than the original equation.

We shall consider, for example, the equation

$$\epsilon u'' + (1 + \epsilon) u' + u = 0, \qquad u(0) = c_1, \qquad u'(0) = c_2, \qquad (28.4)$$

with $\epsilon > 0$. If we set $\epsilon = 0$, we are left with the first-order equation

$$u' + u = 0, \qquad u(0) = c_1, \qquad u'(0) = c_2. \qquad (28.5)$$

These initial conditions are inconsistent unless $c_1 = -c_2$.

The solution to the original equation is given by

$$u = \frac{\epsilon(c_1 + c_2)\,e^{-t/\epsilon}}{(\epsilon - 1)} - \frac{(c_2\epsilon + c_1)\,e^{-t}}{(\epsilon - 1)}, \qquad (28.6)$$

with

$$u' = \frac{-(c_1 + c_2)\,e^{-t/\epsilon}}{(\epsilon - 1)} + \frac{(c_2\epsilon + c_1)\,e^{-t}}{(\epsilon - 1)}. \qquad (28.7)$$

As $\epsilon \to +0$, $u \to c_1 e^{-t}$, but u' has the following *discontinuous* behavior

$$\lim_{\epsilon \to 0} u' = -c_1 e^{-t}, \qquad t > 0,$$

$$= c_2, \qquad t = 0. \qquad (28.8)$$

Hence

$$\lim_{t \to 0}\left(\lim_{\epsilon \to 0} u'\right) \neq \lim_{\epsilon \to 0}\left(\lim_{t \to 0} u'\right). \qquad (28.9)$$

EXERCISE

28.1. Study the behavior of $u' + u = \epsilon u''^2$ as $\epsilon \to 0$.

COMMENTS AND BIBLIOGRAPHY

Equations of this nature occur in the study of boundary layer phenomena in hydrodynamics and in other parts of mathematical physics. A great deal of work has been done in recent years unraveling some of the many perplexing features of equations of the foregoing type, but much more remains to be done. See

A. Erdelyi, "Singular Perturbations," *Bull. Am. Math. Soc.*, **68**, 420-424, 1962.

L. Flatto and N. Levinson, "Periodic Solutions of Singularly Perturbed Systems," *J. Rat. Mech. and Analysis*, **4**, 943-950, 1955.

W. A. Harris, Jr., "Singular Perturbations of a Boundary Value Problem for a Nonlinear System of differential equations," *Duke Math. J.*, **29**, 429-444, 1962.

J. J. Levin and N. Levinson, "Singular Perturbations of Nonlinear Systems of Differential Equations and an Associated Boundary Layer Equation," *J. Rat. Mech. and Analysis*, **3**, 247-270, 1954.

W. Wasow, "Singular Perturbations of Boundary Value Problems for Nonlinear Differential Equations of the Second Order," *Comm. Pure and Appl. Math.*, **9**, 93-113, 1956.

where many additional references may be found.

29. Equations with Small Time Lags

In many parts of mathematics proper, mathematical physics and control theory, one encounters equations of the form

$$u'(t) + au(t - \epsilon) + bu(t) = 0, \tag{29.1}$$

or

$$u''(t) + au(t - \epsilon) = 0, \tag{29.2}$$

with initial conditions now holding over the interval $[0, \epsilon]$.

If the time lag ϵ is small, it is tempting to disregard ϵ entirely, or to take account of first-order effects by expanding and neglecting terms of $O(\epsilon^2)$. Thus (29.1) and (29.2) become, respectively,

$$u'(t) - a\epsilon u'(t) + (b - a\epsilon) u(t) = 0,$$
$$u''(t) - a\epsilon u'(t) + au(t) = 0. \tag{29.3}$$

On the other hand, if we write (29.2) as

$$u''(t + \epsilon) + au(t) = 0, \tag{29.4}$$

the result corresponding to (29.3) is

$$\epsilon u'''(t) + u''(t) + au(t) = 0. \tag{29.5}$$

As pointed out in the preceding section, formal procedures of this type can lead to difficulties.

EXERCISES

29.1. Compare the solutions of

(a) $u'(t) + au(t) = 0,$

(b) $u'(t) (1 - a\epsilon) + au(t) = 0,$

(c) $a \dfrac{\epsilon^2}{2} u'' + (1 - a\epsilon) u'(t) + au(t) = 0,$

with appropriate initial conditions.

COMMENTS AND BIBLIOGRAPHY

In the case of constant coefficients, linear differential-difference equations can be solved explicitly by means of Laplace transform techniques; see

R. Bellman and K. L. Cooke, *Differential-difference Equations*, New York: Academic Press Inc., 1962.

Little work has been devoted to the study of the behavior of the solutions of differential-difference equations as the retardation approaches zero. See

R. Bellman and K. L. Cooke, "On the Limit of Solutions of Differential-difference Equations as the Retardation Approaches Zero," *Proc. Nat. Acad. Sci. US*, **45**, 1026-1028, 1959.

S. Sugiyama, "Continuity Properties of the Retardation in the Theory of Differential-difference Equations," *Proc. Japan Acad.*, **37**, 179-182, 1961.

For results concerning equations with variable retardation, see

D. Myskis, *Linear Differential Equations with Retarded Argument*, Moscow, 1951; German translation: Berlin: Deutscher Verlag, 1955.

MISCELLANEOUS REFERENCES

Let us merely refer to a most important area that we will not have space to discuss in this volume; the use of summability methods to obtain or accelerate convergence. See

D. Shanks, "Nonlinear transformations of divergent and slowly convergent sequences," *J. Math. and Phys.*, **34**, 1-42, 1955.

G. G. Bilodeau, "On the use of summability to increase the rate of convergence of series," *J. Math. and Phys.*, **40**, 289-299, 1961.

R. Bellman and R. Kalaba, "A note on nonlinear summability techniques in invariant imbedding," *J. Math. Analysis and Appl.*, **6**, 465-472, 1963.

For a different type of perturbation based upon continued fractions, see

R. Bellman and J. M. Richardson, "A new formalism in perturbation theory using continued fractions," *Proc. Nat. Acad. Sci. US*, **48**, 1913-1915, 1962.

[2]

Periodic Solutions of Nonlinear Differential Equations and Renormalization Techniques

1. Introduction

In the previous chapter we were primarily concerned with the equilibrium of solutions, in the study of solutions that tended to zero with increasing time, and in the manner in which this occurred. In this chapter we study behavior of entirely different type—periodicity of solutions. This is a vast domain of the theory of differential equations with many formidable stretches. We shall attempt to illuminate only one small area—the derivation of approximations to periodic solutions of second-order nonlinear differential equations of the form

$$u'' + u + \epsilon g(u, u') = 0, \qquad (1.1)$$

where ϵ is, as usual, a small parameter.

The classical work of Poincaré, Lyapunov, Birkhoff, and others had its origin in celestial mechanics, the motion of the heavenly spheres. The low frequency of oscillation, which is to say the relatively long periods, permitted the use of relatively simple techniques. Errors that arose could always be corrected years or centuries later. The situation changed drastically with the development of the electronic oscillator with megacycle frequency. The work of Van der Pol on the equations of the multivibrator

$$u'' + \epsilon(u^2 - 1)\, u' + u = 0 \qquad (1.2)$$

triggered a new wave of research that led to new and significant developments.

To illustrate some of the phenomena associated with nonlinearity, we shall treat both the foregoing equation and the equation of the nonlinear spring

$$u'' + u + \epsilon u^3 = 0. \qquad (1.3)$$

There are surprises in store. Pedestrian perturbation techniques blithely applied produce nonperiodic and even unbounded representations of the solutions.

We shall present only a few of the many powerful methods now available, and proceed in a purely formal way. The reader interested in rigorous presentations and in other techniques may consult the works referred to at the end of the chapter.

COMMENTS AND BIBLIOGRAPHY

For the mathematical theory of celestial mechanics, see

A. Wintner, *Celestial Mechanics*, Princeton, New Jersey: Princeton University Press.

For a discussion of periodic solutions of nonlinear partial differential equations, with numerous references, see

T. Taniuti, "On Wave Propagation in Nonlinear Fields," *Progr. of Theoretical Phys.*, Supplement No. 9, 69-128, 1958.

See also the expository paper by Von Karman referred to in Chapter One at the end of Section 1.

The major work in the area by one of the pioneers in the field is

N. Minorsky, *Nonlinear Oscillations*, Princeton, N. J.: D. Von Nostrand Co., 1962.

All students of these problems will wish to refer to this book.

2. Secular Terms

Let us begin by following a procedure that caused a certain amount of grief to the early investigators of celestial mechanics. Let us assume that we wish to find the solution of

$$u'' + u + \epsilon u^3 = 0 \tag{2.1}$$

close to the solution $u_0 = a \cos t$ of the unperturbed equation, $u'' + u = 0$. Writing, as we have been accustomed,

$$u = u_0 + \epsilon u_1 + \epsilon^2 u_2 + \cdots, \tag{2.2}$$

and equating coefficients of ϵ, we obtain the equation

$$u_1'' + u_1 + a^3 \cos^3 t = 0, \tag{2.3}$$

for u_1 and corresponding equations for u_2, u_3, $\cdots$. To solve this in the usual fashion, we write

$$\cos^3 t = \frac{\cos 3t + 3 \cos t}{4}.$$

The forcing term $\cos 3t/4$ produces a well-behaved particular solution, $-\cos 3t/32$, but the forcing term $3 \cos t/4$ introduces difficulties. A particular solution corresponding to this term is

$$\tfrac{3}{4}(t \sin t + 2 \cos t). \tag{2.4}$$

We find then that $u_1(t)$ (supposedly a small correction to the periodic function $u_0(t)$) is not only nonperiodic, it is in addition unbounded as t increases. The term $3t \sin t/4$ is called a *secular term*.

We see, rather to our astonishment, that a naive application of trusted perturbation techniques leads to a rather absurd result. What is the crux of the difficulty? The answer lies in the observation that the nonlinearity exemplified by ϵu^3 affects not only the *amplitude* of the solution, but also the *frequency*. In order to find the periodic solution close to the curve $u_0 = a \cos t$ in phase space, that is, in the (u, u') plane, we must take account of these facts, easily observed experimentally and intuitively clear.

EXERCISES

2.1. Apply the straightforward perturbation procedure to the solution of

$$u'' + (1 + \epsilon)^2 u = 0.$$

2.2. Consider the linear system

$$u' = v, \qquad v' = -(1 + \epsilon)^2 u$$

with the periodic solutions

$$u^2(1 + \epsilon)^2 + v^2 = k^2.$$

Obtain these from the corresponding curves of $u' = v$, $v' = -u$ by a perturbation technique.

2.3. The solution $u_0 = c_1 \cos t$ corresponds to the curve $x^2 + y^2 = c_1^2$ in the phase plane $x = u_0(t)$, $y = u_0'(t)$. Can one obtain a nearby curve

$$f(x, y) = x^2 + y^2 + \epsilon g_1(x, y) + \epsilon^2 g_2(x, y) + \cdots = c_1^2$$

where g_1, g_2, $\cdots$, are determined by the conditions that

$$\frac{df}{dt} = \frac{\partial f}{\partial x}\frac{dx}{dt} + \frac{\partial f}{\partial y}\frac{dy}{dt} = y\frac{\partial f}{\partial x} - (x + \epsilon x^3)\frac{\partial f}{\partial y} = 0?$$

2.4. Show that a first integral of $u'' + u + \epsilon u^3 = 0$ is $u'^2 + u^2 + \epsilon u^4/4 = k$, and thus obtain approximate expressions for the periodic solutions and their periods.

2.5. Given the equation

$$x'' + f(x)\, x' + g(x) = 0,$$

where

$$f(x) = (n + 2)\, bx^n - 2a, \qquad g(x) = x[c + (bx^n - n)^2]$$

show that the solution is

$$x = \cos(p + wt)\left\{ qe^{-nat} + nbe^{-nat} \int_0^t e^{na\theta} \cos{}^n(p + w\theta)\, d\theta \right\}^{-1/n},$$

$$c = w^2.$$

(R. A. Smith, "A Simple Nonlinear Oscillation," *JLMS*, **36**, 33-34, 1961.)

3. Renormalization à la Lindstedt

To account for the fact that the frequency is altered, we change the independent variable, writing

$$t = s(1 + c_1\epsilon + c_2\epsilon^2 + \cdots). \tag{3.1}$$

Then the equation of (2.1) becomes

$$\frac{d^2u}{ds^2} + (1 + c_1\epsilon + c_2\epsilon^2 + \cdots)^2 (u + \epsilon u^3) = 0 \tag{3.2}$$

or

$$\frac{d^2u}{ds^2} + u + \epsilon(2c_1u + u^3) + \epsilon^2(\cdots) + \cdots = 0. \tag{3.3}$$

We can now invoke the perturbation technique—with care. We write

$$u = a\cos s + \epsilon u_1(s) + \epsilon^2 u_2(s) + \cdots. \tag{3.4}$$

Then $u_1(s)$ satisfies the equation

$$u_1'' + u_1 = -(2\epsilon_1 u_0 + u_0^3)$$

$$= -(2ac_1\cos s + a^3\cos^3 s). \tag{3.5}$$

The unknown coefficient c_1 is determined by the condition that no secular term is allowed to arise from this equation. Using the expression for $\cos^3 s$ in (2.8), we see that the complete forcing term is

$$- \left(2ac_1 \cos s + \frac{a^3(\cos 3s + 3 \cos s)}{4} \right). \tag{3.6}$$

Hence we choose c_1 so that

$$2ac_1 + \frac{3a^3}{4} = 0, \tag{3.7}$$

or

$$c_1 = -\frac{3a^2}{8}.$$

Hence, (3.5) assumes the form

$$u_1'' + u_1 = -\frac{a^3(\cos 3s)}{4}, \tag{3.8}$$

with the solution

$$u_1 = \frac{a^3(\cos 3s)}{32}, \tag{3.9}$$

taking $u_1(0) = u_1'(0) = 0$ so that u, as given by (3.4) has the same initial conditions as $u_0 = a \cos s$.

Thus

$$u = a \cos s + \frac{a\epsilon(\cos 3s)}{32} + 0(\epsilon^2), \tag{3.10}$$

with

$$s = \frac{t}{1 - 3a^2\epsilon/8} + 0(\epsilon^2). \tag{3.11}$$

Observe that, as was expected in this case, the change in frequency is dependent upon the amplitude.

EXERCISES

3.1. Following the same procedure, determine the coefficient c_2, and the function $u_2(s)$.

3.2. For the equation $u'' + u + \epsilon g(u) = 0$, determine the change in frequency to terms in $0(\epsilon^2)$ in terms of the function $g(u)$, using the foregoing technique.

3.3. Obtain the result directly from the first integral

$$u'^2 + u^2 + 2\epsilon \int_0^u g(u_1)\, du_1 = c_3.$$

4. The Van der Pol Equation

Let us now apply the same renormalization technique to the study of the equation

$$u'' + \epsilon(u^2 - 1) u' + u = 0. \tag{4.1}$$

As noted above, this equation arose in the study of the multivibrator, an electronic oscillator subsequently to play an important role in radar circuits. An equivalent equation had been studied by Rayleigh.

Changing the independent variable as above, we obtain the equation

$$\frac{d^2u}{ds^2} + \epsilon(u^2 - 1) \frac{du}{ds} (1 + c_1\epsilon + c_2\epsilon^2 + \cdots) + (1 + c_1\epsilon + c_2\epsilon^2 + \cdots)^2 u = 0. \tag{4.2}$$

Setting

$$u = a \cos s + \epsilon u_1(s) + \cdots, \tag{4.3}$$

we see that u_1 satisfies the equation

$$\frac{d^2u_1}{ds^2} + u_1 + (2c_1 \cos s - a \sin s \, (a^2 \cos^2 s - 1)) = 0. \tag{4.4}$$

To avoid the presence of a secular term, we want the forcing term in (4.4) to possess no term in $\cos s$ or $\sin s$. Since

$$\int_0^{2\pi} \sin s(a^2 \cos^2 s - 1) \cos s \, ds = 0, \tag{4.5}$$

the only term in $\cos s$ is the term $2c_1 \cos s$. Hence $c_1 = 0$, which means that the change in frequency is a second order effect, negligible for small ϵ.* The coefficient of $\sin s$ is given by the expression

$$\frac{1}{\pi} \int_0^{2\pi} \sin^2 s(a^2 \cos^2 s - 1) \, ds. \tag{4.6}$$

Hence the amplitude a must satisfy the condition

$$a^2 \int_0^{2\pi} \sin^2 s \cos^2 s \, ds = \int_0^{2\pi} \sin^2 s \, ds, \tag{4.7}$$

or $a^2 = 2$, to terms which are $0(\epsilon)$.

* As we shall point out below, it turns out to be surprisingly small for all $\epsilon > 0$.

But this is an astonishing result. It tells us that of the nondenumerable totality of periodic solutions of the linear equation

$$u'' + u = 0, \tag{4.8}$$

only *one*, that represented by the circle

$$x^2 + y^2 = 2 \tag{4.9}$$

in the phase plane, can be perturbed into a periodic solution of (4.1). The others yield no periodic solution of (4.1), no matter how small ϵ is. Thus the presence of the slightest amount of nonlinearity effectively rejects large classes of solutions, in this case all but one solution.

EXERCISES

4.1. Obtain the second order change in frequency and the first order change in amplitude, following the foregoing technique.

4.2. Consider the equation

$$u'' + \epsilon h(u)\, u' + u = 0.$$

How should $h(u)$ be chosen so that we obtain a given set of periodic solutions,

$$u = c_i \cos t, \qquad i = 1, 2, \cdots, N,$$

as first order approximations for small ϵ?

4.3. If we have a sequence of periodic orbits as pictured in Fig. 3, can they all represent stable periodic solutions, and if not, which ones are stable and which ones unstable?

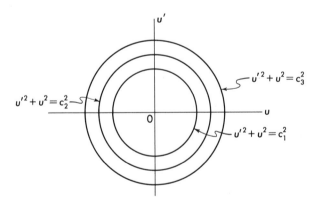

Fig. 3

COMMENTS AND BIBLIOGRAPHY

For a rigorous derivation of the perturbation series, and for a topological discussion of periodic solutions in general, see

L. Cesari, *Asymptotic Behavior and Stability Problems in Ordinary Differential Equations*, Berlin, Springer-Verlag, 1959.

S. Lefschetz, *Lectures on Differential Equations*, Princeton, N.J.: Princeton University Press, 1946.

J. J. Stoker, *Nonlinear Vibrators in Mechanical and Electrical Systems*, New York: Interscience Publishers, Inc., 1950.

H. Poincaré, *Méthodes nouvelles de la mécanique céleste*, Vols. I, II, III, Paris: Gauthier-Villars, 1892.

R. Mori, *Analytical Design of Vacuum Tube Blocking Oscillator*, Tokyo: Electro-technical Laboratory, No. 616, 1961.

The preceding results have a great deal of significance as far as quantum mechanics is concerned, as Minorsky and the author discussed in conversations in 1946. They show that an infinitesimal amount of nonlinearity both quantifies phase space and determines the amplitude of periodic motion, which is to say of orbits. Hence, the stable *limit cycles* (as the periodic solutions are called) can represent stable states. The presence of interlarded unstable limit cycles means that energy is required to perturb the orbit from one stable state to another. The extreme stability of the stable cycles explains why no transit time is observed, and perhaps dissipates a certain amount of mysticism about instantaneous change of state.

These ideas have recently gained prominence. See

Andrade e Silva, Joao, Fer Francis, Lenuste Philippe, Lochak, Georges, "Non-linéarité, cycles limites et quantification," *C. R. Acad. Sci. Paris*, **251**, 2662-2664, 1960.

and

Duerr-Heisenberg-Mitter-Schlieder-Yamazaki, "Zur Theorie der Elementar-teilchen," *Zeit für Naturforsch*, Bd. 14a, 441-485, 1959.

5. The Shohat Expansion

Let us now employ a device due to Shohat that yields results that are accurate not only for small ϵ but apparently for all $\epsilon > 0$. Let us take the equation

$$u'' + \epsilon(u^2 - 1)\,u' + u = 0 \tag{5.1}$$

and (to keep the notation and values consistent with Shohat's paper) set

$$t = \frac{s}{f(\epsilon)}, \qquad f(\epsilon) = 1 + a_1\epsilon + a_2\epsilon^2 + \cdots. \tag{5.2}$$

The new equation takes the form

$$f^2(\epsilon)\frac{d^2u}{ds^2} + f(\epsilon)\,\epsilon(u^2 - 1)\frac{du}{ds} + u = 0. \tag{5.3}$$

If we proceed in the fashion described above, we obtain the Lindstedt expansion, valid for small ϵ. Keeping in mind that we know a priori from theoretical analysis that a periodic solution exists for all $\epsilon > 0$, and that $f(\epsilon) \sim 1/\epsilon$ as $\epsilon \to \infty$, let us introduce the change of variable

$$r = \frac{\epsilon}{1 + \epsilon}, \tag{5.4}$$

or

$$\epsilon = r - r^2 + r^3 - \cdots,$$
$$\epsilon f(\epsilon) = r + c_2 r^2 + c_3 r^3 + \cdots,$$
$$u = \cos s + r u_1(s) + r^2 u_2(s) + \cdots. \tag{5.5}$$

Substituting in (5.3) and applying the Lindstedt technique described above in Section 3, we find that

$$c_2 = 1, \qquad c_3 = \frac{15}{16}, \qquad c_4 = \frac{13}{16}. \tag{5.6}$$

To illustrate the remarkable accuracy of what is supposed only to be a perturbation expansion, we shall consider the following sets of values taken, respectively, from Shohat's paper, a paper of Van der Pol in which approximation integration techniques are used, and papers by Urabe and Dorodnicyn, where the most accurate values appear in Table I. The values in the "Shohat" are obtained using only four terms in the series expansion.

TABLE I

ϵ	Shohat	Van der Pol	Urabe-Dorodnicyn
1.0	0.93	0.90	0.92
2.0	0.77	0.78	0.81
8.0	0.35	0.39	0.39
10.0	0.30	0.31	0.33

Examining the foregoing values, it is tempting to conjecture that the Shohat series converges for all $\epsilon \geq 0$.

What is rather surprising about the remarkable range of validity of (5.5) is that the actual asymptotic expansion for $f(\epsilon)$ as $\epsilon \to \infty$ has a very complex transcendental structure.

EXERCISES

5.1. Apply the same techniques to the equation

$$u'' + \epsilon(u^2 - 1)\, u' + u = a \cos \omega t$$

to find a solution of period $2\pi/\omega$.

5.2. The equation

$$u'' + u + \epsilon u^3 = 0$$

leads to the first integral $u'^2 + u^2 + \epsilon u^4/4 = k$, and thus to an explicit solution in terms of elliptic functions. Obtain in this way the exact series expansion for the period of the periodic solution as a function of ϵ and k and determine its radius of convergence.

5.3. What relation is between the solution of

$$u'' + u(t + \epsilon(u^2 - 1)) = 0$$

and the solution of the Van der Pol equation?

COMMENTS AND BIBLIOGRAPHY

The long overlooked results of Shohat were originally given in

J. Shohat, "On Van der Pol's and Related Nonlinear Differential Equations," *J. Appl. Phys.*, **15**, 568-574, 1944.

The results are reproduced (with some further applications of the idea that we shall discuss in Chapter 3) in

R. Bellman, "On Perturbation Methods Involving Expansions in Terms of a Parameter," *Q. Appl. Math.*, **13**, 195-200, 1955.

——, "Perturbation Methods Applied to Nonlinear Mechanics," *Amer. Soc. Mech. Engineers*, Paper No. 55-APM-33.

For a rigorous treatment and the asymptotic behavior for large ϵ, see

P. Brock, "The Nature of Solution of a Rayleigh Type Forced Vibration Equation with a Large Coefficient of Damping," *J. Appl. Phys.*, **24**, 1004-1007, 1953.

K. Munakata, "Use of Elliptic Functions for Nonlinear Equations," *J. Phys. Soc. Japan*, **7**, 1952.

R. A. Smith, "On the Singularities of $y'' + f(y) y' + g(y) = f(x)$ in the complex Plane," *Proc. London Math. Soc.*, **3**, 498-512 (1953).

R. A. Struble and J. E. Fletcher, "General Perturbational Solution of the Harmonically Forced Van der Pol Equation," *J. Math. Phys.*, **2**, 880-887, 1961.

———, "General Perturbational Solution of the Mathieu Equation," *J. Soc. Indust. Appl. Math.*, **10**, 314-328, 1962.

M. Urabe, "Periodic Solutions of Van der Pol's Equation with Damping Coefficient $\lambda = 0 \sim 10$," *IRE Trans.*, PGCT, **CT-7**, 382-386, 1960.

———, "Remarks on Periodic Solutions of Van der Pol's Equation," *J. Sci. Hiroshima Univ.*, Ser. A, **24**, 197-199, 1960.

The values for the amplitude of the periodic solution as a function of ϵ may be found here. They show that the amplitude varies by at most a few per cent over the entire range $0 < \epsilon < \infty$.

For a systematic study of the use of elliptic functions in the exact and approximate solutions of the equations

$$u'' + u + bu^3 = a \cos \omega t,$$

and for the expansions of the period in terms of various parameters, see

C. S. Hsu, "On the Application of Elliptic Functions in Nonlinear Forced Oscillations," *Q. Appl. Math.*, **17**, 393-407, 1960.

For applications of these ideas to other types of functional equations, emphasizing the connections with summability theory, see

R. Bellman, "On Perturbation Methods Involving Expansions in Terms of a Parameter," *Q. Appl. Math.*, **13**, 195-200, 1955.

R. Bellman, "Perturbation Methods Applied to Nonlinear Dynamics," *Amer. Soc. Mech. Engrs. Paper No.* 55-APM-33.

R. Bellman, "A Note on the Summability of Formal Solutions of Linear Integral Equations," *Duke Math. J.*, **17**, 53-55, 1950.

6. Perturbation Series for the Period

Let us now suppose that the nonlinear differential equation

$$u'' + u + \epsilon g(u, u') = 0 \tag{6.1}$$

(where $g(u, u')$ is taken to be an analytic function of its arguments, say a polynomial) possesses a periodic solution through every point of the phase plane,

$u(0) = c_1$, $u'(0) = c_2$ (as opposed to the Van der Pol equation which, as we know, possesses only *one* periodic solution). Let the period T be represented as a function of c_1 and c_2, $T = T(c_1, c_2)$. Then, let us write, in the neighborhood of $\epsilon = 0$,

$$T(c_1, c_2) = 2\pi + \epsilon f_1(c_1, c_2) + \epsilon^2 f_2(c_1, c_2) + \cdots. \tag{6.2}$$

What information can we obtain concerning the form of the functions f_1, f_2, $\cdots$? Let us apply functional equation techniques. Following the periodic solution for an infinitesimal time Δ from a starting point (c_1, c_2) in the phase plane, we obtain the relation

$$T(c_1, c_2) = T(c_1 + c_2\Delta, c_2 - \Delta(c_1 + \epsilon g(c_1, c_2))) + o(\Delta). \tag{6.3}$$

Passing to the limit as $\Delta \to 0$, we obtain the partial differential equation

$$c_2 \frac{\partial T}{\partial c_1} - (c_1 + \epsilon g(c_1, c_2)) \frac{\partial T}{\partial c_2} = 0. \tag{6.4}$$

Using the expression of (6.2) and equating coefficients, we thus derive a system of partial differential equations from which some results can be deduced, as we indicate in the exercises and Fig. 4 which follow,

$$c_2 \frac{\partial f_1}{\partial c_1} - c_1 \frac{\partial f_1}{\partial c_2} = 0,$$

$$c_2 \frac{\partial f_2}{\partial c_1} - c_1 \frac{\partial f_2}{\partial c_2} - g(c_1, c_2) \frac{\partial f_1}{\partial c_2} = 0, \tag{6.5}$$

$$\vdots$$

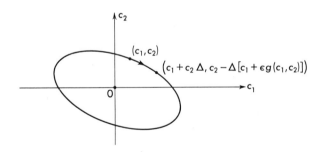

Fig. 4

EXERCISES

6.1. Consider the equation

$$u'' + u + \epsilon g(u) = 0.$$

Show that

$$T(c_1, c_2) = T(\bar{c}_1, 0) = T(0, \bar{c}_2)$$

where $\bar{c}_1$ and $\bar{c}_2$ are determined by the relations

$$\bar{c}_1^2 + 2\epsilon G(\bar{c}_1) = c_2^2 + c_1^2 + 2\epsilon G(c_1),$$

$$\bar{c}_2^2 = c_2^2 + c_1^2 + \epsilon G(c_1),$$

with

$$G(u) = \int_0^u g(u_1) \, du_1 .$$

6.2. Hence, for the foregoing equation show that

$$f_1(c_1, c_2) = f_1(0, (c_1^2 + c_2^2)^{1/2}),$$

$$f_2(c_1, c_2) = f_2(0, (c_1^2 + c_2^2)^{1/2}) + \frac{G(c_1)}{(c_1^2 + c_2^2)^{1/2}} \frac{\partial f_1}{\partial c_2} (0, (c_1^2 + c_2^2)^{1/2}),$$

and so on.

6.3. Consider next the case where $g(u) = u^{2n+1}$. Show that

$$T(c_1, c_2) = T(c_1, c_2, \epsilon) = T\left(\frac{c_1}{k}, \frac{c_2}{k}, \epsilon k^{2n-1}\right).$$

6.4. Hence show that

$$f_1(c_1, c_2) = k^{2n-1} f_1\left(\frac{c_1}{k}, \frac{c_2}{k}\right),$$

$$f_2(c_1, c_2) = k^{4n-2} f_2\left(\frac{c_1}{k}, \frac{c_2}{k}\right),$$

$$\vdots$$

6.5. Continuing in this vein, show that

$$f_1(c_1, c_2) = a_1(c_1^2 + c_2^2)^{(2n-1)/2},$$

where a_1 is a constant and obtain an analogous expression for $f_2(c_1, c_2)$.

6.6. Obtain corresponding results for the equation

$$u'' + u + \epsilon_1 u^3 + \epsilon_2 u^5 + \cdots + \epsilon_{2k+1} u^{2k+1} = 0,$$

upon writing

$$T(c_1, c_2) = T(c_1, c_2, \epsilon_1, \epsilon_2, \cdots, \epsilon_{2k+1}).$$

COMMENTS AND BIBLIOGRAPHY

For the previous results, see

R. Bellman, R. Kalaba, and R. Vasudevan, "A Note on Perturbation Series," *J. Math. Analysis and Appl.*, **4**, 341-345, 1962.

It appears to be quite difficult to determine the constant a_1 using the foregoing techniques.

For an interesting related paper, see

J. J. Levin and S. S. Shatz, "Nonlinear Oscillations of Fixed Period," *J. Math. Analysis and Appl.*, to appear.

7. Self-consistent Techniques

Let us now describe a type of approximation that plays an important role in modern mathematical physics but that has as yet been little investigated or utilized in purely mathematical contexts. To illustrate this new method, let us begin with the Van der Pol equation

$$u'' + \epsilon(u^2 - 1) u' + u = 0, \tag{7.1}$$

and approximate to the term $(u^2 - 1) u'$ by a linear combination of u and u',

$$(u^2 - 1) u' \simeq a_1 u + a_2 u', \tag{7.2}$$

where a_1 and a_2 are constants. We shall measure the deviation between the exact and approximate quantities, by means of the expression

$$\int_0^{2\pi} ((u^2 - 1) u' - a_1 u - a_2 u')^2 \, dt. \tag{7.3}$$

Having done this, we naturally choose a_1 and a_2 to minimize this function. The equations for the minimizing values of a_1 and a_2 are

$$\int_0^{2\pi} ((u^2 - 1) u' - a_1 u - a_2 u') u \, dt = 0,$$

$$\int_0^{2\pi} ((u^2 - 1) u' - a_1 u - a_2 u') u' \, dt = 0. \tag{7.4}$$

If u is periodic of period 2π, we have

$$\int_0^{2\pi} (u^2 - 1) uu' \, dt = 0, \qquad \int_0^{2\pi} u'u \, dt = 0. \tag{7.5}$$

We see from the first equation that $a_1 = 0$. Hence, the second equation yields the equation

$$a_2 = \frac{\int_0^{2\pi} (u^2 - 1) u'^2 \, dt}{\int_0^{2\pi} u'^2 \, dt}. \tag{7.6}$$

Using this approximation, the equation of (7.1) then takes the form

$$u'' + \epsilon a_2 u' + u = 0. \tag{7.7}$$

We observe that a_2, as defined by (7.6), depends upon the unknown solution u. Consequently, we must take some further steps before (7.7) is useful.

Let us now introduce the constraint that we are looking only for a periodic solution. It follows that a_2 must equal zero, a self-consistency condition. Taking u to have the form $a \cos t$, we obtain the familiar relation

$$\int_0^{2\pi} (u^2 - 1) u'^2 \, dt = 0 = \int_0^{2\pi} (a^2 \cos^2 t - 1) \sin^2 t \, dt, \tag{7.8}$$

whence

$$a^2 = \frac{\int_0^{2\pi} \sin^2 t \, dt}{\int_0^{2\pi} \sin^2 t \cos^2 t \, dt} = 2. \tag{7.9}$$

If we had not known in advance that the period was 2π, to first-order terms, we would have used as a measure of approximation

$$\lim_{T \to \infty} \frac{1}{T} \int_0^T ((u^2 - 1) u' - a_1 u - a_2 u')^2 \, dt. \tag{7.10}$$

This is an important technique in connection with the application of the foregoing technique to higher-dimensional problems where the solutions may be almost periodic.

EXERCISES

7.1. Apply the same procedure to the study of the equations

$$u'' + u + \epsilon u^3 = 0 \quad \text{and} \quad u'' + u + \epsilon g(u) = 0.$$

7.2. Why is setting $a_2 = 0$ by way of equation (7.6) different from setting it equal to zero from the very beginning?

COMMENTS AND BIBLIOGRAPHY

The results of the foregoing section are particular cases of a general technique given in

R. Bellman and J. M. Richardson, "Renormalization Techniques and Mean-square Averaging—I: Deterministic Equations," *Proc. Nat. Acad. Sci. US*, **47**, 1191-1194, 1961.

———— and ————, "Perturbation Techniques," *Symposium on Nonlinear Oscillations*, Kiev, USSR, 1961.

For a discussion of other averaging techiques, see

N. Kryloff and N. Bogoliuboff, "Introduction to Nonlinear Mechanics," *Annals of Mathematics Studies*, No. 11, Princeton, N. J.: Princeton University Press, 1947,

and numerous other references given in the books by Cesari and Minorsky cited above.

See also

S. P. Diliberto, "Perturbation Theorems for Periodic Surfaces II," *Rend. Circolo Mat.*, Serie II, **10**, 113-161, 1961.

J. W. Tukey, "Linearization of Solutions in Supersonic Flow," *Q. Appl. Math.*, **5**, 361-365, 1947.

It may be worthwhile here also to mention the very useful idea of Caplygin that is to bound the solutions of nonlinear differential equations by means of solutions of associated linear equations. See the references in

E. F. Beckenbach and R. Bellman, *Inequalities*, Ergebnisse Der. Math., Berlin: Springer-Verlag, 1961.

8. Carleman Linearization

As a step towards improving the approximation obtained by means of the techniques described above, let us describe a linearization of nonlinear differential equations apparently first used by Carleman. To simplify the algebra and notation, we shall restrict our attention to the simple Riccati equation

$$\frac{du}{dt} = -u + u^2, \qquad u(0) = c, \tag{8.1}$$

once again ignoring the fact that this equation can be solved explicitly. We introduce the variables

$$u_k(t) = u^k, \qquad k = 1, 2, \cdots. \tag{8.2}$$

Then

$$\frac{du_k}{dt} = ku^{k-1}\frac{du}{dt} = ku^{k-1}(-u + u^2) = -ku_k + ku_{k+1}. \tag{8.3}$$

We have thus established a correspondence between the first-order nonlinear equation of (8.1) and the infinite system of linear equations of (8.3).

EXERCISES

8.1. Writing $u'' + u + \epsilon u^3 = 0$ in the form of a system

$$u' = v,$$
$$v' = -u - \epsilon u^3,$$

obtain an infinite system of linear equations for the quantities $u^m v^n$. Carry out a similar linearization for the Van der Pol equation.

8.2. Attaching the initial values $u_k(0) = c^k$, study the solution of (8.3) by introducing the generating function

$$u(r, t) = \sum_{k=1}^{\infty} u_k(t)\, r^k.$$

9. Finite Closure

It is tempting to approximate to the solution of the infinite system of (8.3), and thus to the solution of the original nonlinear equation, by cutting off at a finite value of N and using the resultant finite linear system

$$\frac{du_k}{dt} = -ku_k + ku_{k+1}, \qquad u_k(0) = c^k, \qquad k = 1, 2, \cdots, N. \tag{9.1}$$

The method cannot be applied this naively, since the first N equations involve $(N + 1)$ unknown functions. To circumvent this obstacle, we replace u_{N+1} by a function of the first N functions u_i, $i = 1, 2, \cdots, N$, in order to obtain a closed set of equations.

In order to preserve the utility of this approximation scheme, we take u_{N+1} to be a linear function of the u_i,

$$u_{N+1} = \sum_{i=1}^{N} a_{iN} u_i. \tag{9.2}$$

It is now a matter of choosing the coefficients in some expedient fashion. Some of the possible approaches will be discussed below.

EXERCISES

9.1. Consider the case where we set $u_{N+1} = 0$, that is,

$$a_{iN} = 0, \qquad i = 1, 2, \cdots, N.$$

The resulting system of linear equations is

$$\frac{dv_k}{dt} = -kv_k + kv_{k+1}, \qquad k = 1, 2, \cdots, N-1,$$

$$\frac{dv_N}{dt} = -Nv_N,$$

with $v_k(0) = c^k$. Obtain the explicit solution of this system, and compare it with the exact solution of (8.1).

9.2. Show, inductively, that

$$|u_k - v_k| \le (2|c|)^{N+1},$$

without obtaining the explicit solution.

COMMENTS AND BIBLIOGRAPHY

For a more detailed discussion of these matters, and the connections with the classic concepts of stability, see

R. Bellman and J. M. Richardson, "On Some Questions Arising in the Approximate Solution of Nonlinear Differential Equations," *Q. Appl. Math.*, **20**, 333-339, 1963.

10. Closure

Returning to (9.2), we can determine the a_{iN} in a variety of ways. For example, we can choose them so as to minimize

$$\int_0^T \left(u_{N+1} - \sum_{i=1}^N a_{iN}u_i \right)^2 dt, \tag{10.1}$$

a procedure that requires self-consistent methods of the type we met in Section 7, and which we shall discuss again in Section 11.

Alternatively, we can proceed as follows. Let us assume that $|u|$ remains uniformly bounded for the t values of interest, and thus with suitable normalization that $|u| \leq 1$. Starting with the equation

$$\frac{du}{dt} = g(u), \tag{10.2}$$

let us expand $g(u)$, as a function of u, in a series of Legendre polynomials

$$g(u) = \sum_{m=1}^{\infty} a_m p_m(u), \tag{10.3}$$

assuming convergence. Then

$$\frac{d}{dt} p_n(u) = p_n'(u) g(u) = \sum_{m=1}^{\infty} a_{mn} p_m(u). \tag{10.4}$$

If we use the first N equations and neglect the terms in $p_{N+1}(u)$, $p_{N+2}(u)$ and so on, we know that we have automatically made best mean-square fit.

EXERCISES

10.1. Using the fact mentioned above that the amplitude of the periodic solution of the Van der Pol equation does not vary much from 2 for all $\epsilon > 0$, find approximate representations for the periodic solution of

$$u'' + \epsilon(u^2 - 1) u' + u = 0.$$

10.2. In place of mean-square approximation, use the Cebycev norm $\max_{-1 \leq u \leq 1} | \cdots |$, and obtain approximations based upon expansions in Cebycev polynomials.

10.3. Apply the foregoing ideas to systems of nonlinear differential equations

$$\frac{dx_i}{dt} = \sum_{j=1}^{N} a_{ij}x_j + \sum_{j,k=1} a_{ijk}x_jx_k , \qquad x_i(0) = c.$$

For details, see the paper by Bellman and Richardson cited above.

11. Self-consistent Techniques—II

Returning to the equation

$$\frac{du}{dt} = -u + u^2 , \qquad u(0) = c, \tag{11.1}$$

let us approximate to u^2 by a linear combination

$$u^2 \simeq a_1 + a_2 u, \tag{11.2}$$

and choose a_1 and a_2 so as to minimize the expression

$$\int_0^T (u^2 \simeq a_1 u - a_2)^2 \, dt. \tag{11.3}$$

Then a_1 and a_2 are determined by the conditions

$$\int_0^T u^3 \, dt = a_1 \int_0^T u^2 \, dt + a_2 \int_0^T u \, dt,$$

$$\int_0^T u^4 \, dt = a_1 \int_0^T u^3 \, dt + a_2 \int_0^T u^4 \, dt. \tag{11.4}$$

The difficulty we face is that the coefficients a_1 and a_2 depend upon the unknown solution, precisely the function we wish to determine.

To circumvent this obstacle to some extent, we proceed as follows. Solving the linear approximating equation

$$\frac{du}{dt} = -u + a_1 + a_2 u, \qquad u(0) = c, \tag{11.5}$$

we use this function $u = u(a_1, a_2, t)$ in (11.4) and thus obtain a system of simultaneous equations for a_1 and a_2. A constant difficulty in the use of these techniques is the fact that these equations are transcendental equations.

EXERCISES

11.1. Consider the following method of successive approximations. Let $u_0(t)$ be an initial guess, and let $a_1^{(0)}$, $a_2^{(0)}$ be the solution of the simultaneous linear equations of (11.4) when u is replaced by u_0. Let u_1 be determined as the solution of

$$\frac{du_1}{dt} = -u_1 + a_1^{(0)} + a_2^{(0)} u_1, \qquad u_1(0) = c,$$

and then $a_1^{(1)}$, $a_2^{(1)}$ determined from (11.4) with u replaced by u_1, and so on. Under what conditions do the sequences $\{a_1^{(n)}\}$, $\{a_2^{(n)}\}$ converge to the solutions of (11.4)?

11.2. As $T \to \infty$, show that the limiting form of the equations for the unknown constants a_1 and a_2 is

$$\left(\frac{a_2}{1-a_1}\right)^2 - a_1 \left(\frac{a_2}{1-a_1}\right) + a_2 = 0,$$

with

$$u = (c - b) e^{-(1-a_1)t} + b, \qquad b = \frac{a_2}{1 - a_1}.$$

11.3. Hence, show that the approximate solution for u is $u = ce^{-(1-2c/3)t}$, as compared to the exact solution

$$u = \frac{1}{(1 - c) e^t + 1)/c}.$$

A comparison of approximate and exact solutions is appended. See Table II.

TABLE II

COMPARISON OF APPROXIMATE AND EXACT SOLUTIONS ($c = \frac{1}{2}$)

t	u_{exact}	u_{approx}	$u_{\text{approx}}-u_{\text{exact}}$
0	0.500	0.500	0.000
0.1	0.475	0.468	— 0.007
0.2	0.450	0.438	— 0.012
0.5	0.378	0.358	— 0.020
1.0	0.269	0.257	— 0.012
2.0	0.119	0.132	0.013
5.0	0.00669	0.0178	0.0111
10.0	0.000045	0.00063	0.00058

12. Dynamic Programming and Perturbation Series

Suppose that we wish to solve the two-point boundary value problem

$$u'' + u + \epsilon u^3 = 0, \qquad u(0) = c, \qquad u'(T) = 0. \qquad (12.1)$$

Since the solution with $\epsilon = 0$ has the simple form

$$u = \frac{c \cos (t - T)}{\cos T}, \qquad (12.2)$$

we have, assuming $T < \pi/2$, a very simple perturbation scheme based upon the expansion

$$u = \frac{c \cos (t - T)}{\cos T} + \epsilon u_1(t) + \cdots. \qquad (12.3)$$

Each coefficient u_1, u_2 then satisfies a linear differential equation with a two-point boundary condition. Let us proceed in quite a different way, basing our approach upon the fact that (12.1) is the Euler equations associated with the problem of minimizing the functional

$$J(u) = \int_0^T \left(u'^2 - u^2 - \frac{\epsilon u^4}{2} \right) dt \qquad (12.4)$$

over all u satisfying the initial condition $u(0) = c$. To simplify the discussion, we have deliberately used the natural boundary condition $u'(T) = 0$ so that no further attention need be paid to it.

We regard the minimum of $J(u)$ as a function of the initial value c and the end point T and write

$$f(c, T) = \min_u J(u). \qquad (12.5)$$

The theory of dynamic programming then yields the nonlinear partial differential equation

$$\frac{\partial f}{\partial T} = \min_v \left[v^2 - c^2 - \frac{\epsilon c^4}{2} + v \frac{\partial f}{\partial c} \right], \qquad f(c, 0) = 0, \qquad (12.6)$$

or, performing the minimization,

$$\frac{\partial f}{\partial T} = \left[- \frac{(\partial f/\partial c)^2}{4} - c^2 - \tfrac{\scriptscriptstyle \bullet}{}\epsilon c^4 \right]. \qquad (12.7)$$

For $\epsilon = 0$, it is clear that $f(c, T) = c^2 f_1(T)$ where

$$f_1'(T) = - (f_1^2(T) + 1), \qquad f_1(0) = 0. \qquad (12.8)$$

(Or $f_1(T) = - \tan T$, which is incidental.)

We now have two alternatives: We can ignore ϵ and write

$$f(c, T) = c^2 f_1(T) + c^4 f_2(T) + c^6 f_3(T) + \cdots, \qquad (12.9)$$

a power series in c^2, and obtain the differential equations, all of initial value type, for f_2, f_3, and so on, from (12.7); or we can write

$$f(c, T) = c^2 f_1(T) + \epsilon f_2(c, T) + \epsilon^2 f_3(c, T) + \cdots, \qquad (12.10)$$

and obtain linear partial differential equations for f_2, f_3 and so on. Having obtained f, $v(c, T)$ is determined from (12.6), ($v = fc/2$) and thus can obtain the solution u as a function of t.

The advantage of this method as far as higher-order differential equations is concerned as applied to power-series developments in c or ϵ, or both, lies in the fact that the equations we obtain are all of initial value type.

EXERCISES

12.1. Make the change of variable $u = cv$ to replace the dependence upon c and ϵ by dependence upon *one* variable ϵc^2.

COMMENTS AND BIBLIOGRAPHY

For the relevant background in dynamic programming, see

R. Bellman, *Adaptive Control Processes: A Guided Tour*, Princeton, N. J.: Princeton University Press, 1961.

The results given above are contained in

R. Bellman, "A Note on Dynamic Programming and Perturbation Theory," *Proc. Polish National Congress*, September 1962.

13. Temple's Regularization Technique

Let us now consider some further applications of the renormalization technique used to study the periodic solutions of second-order nonlinear differential equations.

To understand the need for these techniques, let us assume that we wish to study the solution of

$$(x + \epsilon u)\frac{du}{dx} + u = 0, \qquad u(1) = 1, \tag{13.1}$$

in the vicinity of $x = 0$. Writing

$$u = u_0 + \epsilon u_1 + \epsilon^2 u_2 + \cdots, \tag{13.2}$$

we see that $u_0 = 1/x$ and that u_1 satisfies the equation

$$x\frac{du_1}{dx} + u_1 - \frac{1}{x^3} = 0, \qquad u_1(1) = 0, \tag{13.3}$$

whence

$$u_1 = \frac{1}{2x} - \frac{1}{2x^3}. \tag{13.4}$$

We see then that the supposed correction term overwhelms the principal term in the neighborhood of $x = 0$. How can we obtain a perturbation series that does not suffer from this defect?

Let us introduce a new parameter t and replace (13.1) by the system of equations

$$\frac{du}{dt} = -u, \qquad u(0) = 1,$$

$$\frac{dx}{dt} = x + \epsilon u, \qquad x(0) = 1. \qquad (13.5)$$

We can now write

$$u = u_0(t) + \epsilon u_1(t) + \cdots,$$
$$x = x_0(t) + \epsilon x_1(t) + \cdots, \qquad (13.6)$$

and proceed in the usual fashion. We see that this method will apply to general equations of the form

$$(x^k + \epsilon g(x, u, \epsilon)) \frac{du}{dx} + h(u, x, \epsilon) = 0, \qquad (13.7)$$

where g and h are analytic in u, x and ϵ in the neighborhood of x and ϵ equal to zero, and in some u region.

EXERCISES

13.1. Study in this way the solutions of

(a) $(x + \epsilon u) \dfrac{du}{dx} + u = 0,$

(b) $(x + \epsilon u) \dfrac{du}{dx} - u = 0,$

(c) $(x + \epsilon u) \dfrac{du}{dx} - u = x,$

(d) $(x^2 + \epsilon u) \dfrac{du}{dx} + 2xu = 1,$

all with initial conditions $u = 1$, $x = 1$.

13.2. Apply the foregoing technique to the equation

$$(x + \epsilon u) \frac{d^2 u}{dx^2} + xu = 0, \qquad u(1) = 1.$$

COMMENTS AND BIBLIOGRAPHY

For the original version of the method, see

M. J. Lighthill, *Phil. Mag.* (7), **40**, 1179-1120, 1949.

―――― and G. Temple, *Proc. Int. Congr. of Math.*, Edinburgh, 1958.

W. Wasow, *J. Rat. Mech. and Analysis*, **4**, 751-767, 1955.

See also

M. F. Pritulo, "On Determining Uniformly Valid Solutions of Differential Equations by the Method of Perturbations of Coordinates," *Prikladnaya Matematika i Mekhanika*, **26**, 444-448, 1962.

14. Elliptic Functions and Mathieu Functions

Let us conclude this chapter with some comments concerning linear equations with periodic coefficients. An equation such as

$$u'' + (a + b \cos t)\, u = 0, \tag{14.1}$$

despite its simple appearance, cannot be solved explicitly in terms of the elementary functions. It defines a new class of transcendental functions, the Mathieu functions.

To treat equations of this nature various approximate techniques have been introduced. Let us discuss one that has been rather neglected. It consists of an initial complication that ultimately provides a simplification.

It was shown by Hermite as a corollary of a general result that the equation

$$u'' + (a + b\, cn\, t)\, u = 0, \tag{14.2}$$

where $cn\, t$ is the Jacobian elliptic function that reduces to $\cos t$ as the modulus $k^2 \to 0$ could be solved explicitly in terms of doubly periodic functions, and thus in terms of the classical doubly periodic functions. The limit of this solution as $k^2 \to 0$ is the solution of (14.1).

Hence we have a systematic way of obtaining approximate solutions to linear equations with periodic coefficients by means of the *exact* solution of linear equations with doubly-periodic coefficients.

COMMENTS AND BIBLIOGRAPHY

For a very complete exposition of the theory of linear differential equations with periodic coefficients, see

V. M. Starzinski, "Survey of Works on Conditions of Stability of the Trivial Solution of a System of Linear Differential Equations with Periodic Coefficients," *Trans. Am. Math. Soc.*, Ser. 2, **1**, 189-239.

The study of linear equations with almost-periodic coefficients is extremely difficult and little is known. For some results pertaining to perturbation theory, see

J. Shtokalo, "On the Theory of Linear Differential Equations with Quasi-periodic Coefficients," *Akad. Nauk. Ukrain, RSR*, **8**, 163-176, 1946.

The work of Hermite is contained in his collected works,

C. Hermite, "Sur quelques applications des fonctions elliptiques," *Œuvres*, **3**, 266-418, 1912.

[3]

The Liouville—WKB Approximation and Asymptotic Series

1. Introduction

The second-order linear differential equation

$$u'' + a^2(t)\, u = 0 \tag{1.1}$$

is one of the basic equations of mathematical physics, arising in such diverse areas as quantum mechanics, diffusion theory, wave propagation, and transmission-line theory, and in numerous other parts of mathematical analysis. Despite its apparent simplicity, it cannot be solved explicitly in terms of quadratures and the elementary functions of analysis. It thus remains a constant challenge to the intuition and resourcefulness of engineers, mathematicians, and physicists to construct approximate solutions specifically geared to particular needs.

In this chapter we shall consider some simple devices due to Liouville and Riccati that make much of the behavior of the solutions of (1.1) quite transparent. We shall next discuss the application of some simple ideas associated with wave propagation that make the WKB approximation (really the Liouville approximation) much more meaningful, and conclude with a discussion of asymptotic series.

2. The Liouville Transformation

One key to the study of the solutions of (1.1) is a simple, but quite ingenious, change of variable due to Liouville. Let us suppose that $a(t) > 0$ for $t \geq 0$ and introduce the new variable

$$s = \int_0^t a(t_1)\, dt_1 . \tag{2.1}$$

80

It is then easy to calculate the derivatives of u regarded as a function of s:

$$\frac{du}{dt} = \frac{ds}{dt}\frac{du}{ds} = a(t)\frac{du}{ds},$$

$$\frac{d^2u}{dt^2} = a'(t)\frac{du}{ds} + a^2(t)\frac{d^2u}{ds^2}. \tag{2.2}$$

Hence, (1.1) becomes

$$\frac{d^2u}{ds^2} + \frac{a'(t)}{a^2(t)}\frac{du}{ds} + u = 0, \tag{2.3}$$

where $a'(t)/a^2(t)$ is a function of s evaluated by means of the relation of (2.1). For example, if $a(t) = t$, we have $s = t^2/2$, and (2.3) becomes

$$\frac{d^2u}{ds^2} + \frac{1}{t^2}\frac{du}{ds} + u = 0, \tag{2.4}$$

or

$$\frac{d^2u}{ds^2} + \frac{1}{2s}\frac{du}{ds} + u = 0. \tag{2.5}$$

EXERCISES

2.1. Carry through the change of variable for the equations

(a) $u'' \pm e^{2bt}u = 0$,

(b) $u'' \pm t^{2n}u = 0$, n both positive and negative.

3. Elimination of Middle Term

The equation of (2.3) is very close in form to the equation

$$u'' + u = 0, \tag{3.1}$$

whose solutions are completely docile. One might suspect that for large s the solutions of (2.3) would mimic those of (3.1). There is certainly a correspondence, but not one that is sufficiently precise for our purposes, nor are all asymptotic properties of the solutions of (3.1) preserved unless various conditions are imposed upon $a(t)$.

In order to study the correspondence with more ease, we wish to eliminate the middle term of (2.3). The desired result is

LEMMA.   The change of dependent variable

$$u = \exp\left(-\tfrac{1}{2}\int_0^t p(s_1)\, ds_1\right) v \tag{3.2}$$

transforms

$$u'' + p(t)\, u' + q(t)\, u = 0 \tag{3.3}$$

into

$$v'' + \left(q(t) - \tfrac{1}{2}p'(t) - \frac{p^2(t)}{4}\right) v = 0. \tag{3.4}$$

The verification of this is direct.

EXERCISES

3.1. Consider the partial differential equation

$$u_{xx} + u_{yy} \pm a^2(x, y)\, u = \mathcal{J}.$$

Replacing x and y by two independent variables s and t, show that the equation takes the form

$$u_{xx}(s_x^2 + s_y^2) + u_{tt}(t_x^2 + t_y^2) + 2u_{st}(s_x t_x + s_y t_y)$$
$$+ u_s(s_{xx} + s_{yy}) + u_t(t_{xx} + t_{yy}) \pm a^2(x, y)\, u = 0.$$

3.2. Suppose that we wish to determine $s(x, y)$ and $t(x, y)$ so that

$$s_x^2 + s_y^2 = a^2(x, y),$$
$$t_x^2 + t_y^2 = a^2(x, y),$$
$$s_x t_x + s_y t_y = 0.$$

Show that this implies that

$$s_x = a(x, y)\cos\varphi, \qquad t_x = a(x, y)\sin\varphi,$$
$$s_y = a(x, y)\sin\varphi, \qquad t_y = -\,a(x, y)\cos\varphi$$

for a function $\varphi(x, y)$.

3.3. Show that φ exists if, and only if,

$$\frac{\partial^2}{\partial x^2}(\log a) + \frac{\partial^2}{\partial y^2}(\log a) = 0;$$

that is, $\log a$ is a harmonic function.

3.4. If $a(x, y)$ satisfies this condition, show that the equation in Exercise 3.1 reduces to $u_{ss} + u_{tt} \pm u = 0$.

3.5. Find explicit solutions of $u_{xx} + u_{yy} \pm e^{2kxy}u = 0$. (For all of these results, see R. Bellman, "On a Liouville transformation of $u_{xx} + u_{yy} \pm a^2(x, y) u = 0$," *Boll. d'Unione Mate.*, **13**, 535-538, 1958.

4. Transform of $u'' + a^2(t) u = 0$

Appying the foregoing transformation to (2.3), we see that the change of variable

$$u = \exp\left(-\tfrac{1}{2} \int^s \frac{a'(t)}{a^2(t)} \, ds_1\right) v \tag{4.1}$$

yields for v the equation

$$v'' + \left(1 - \tfrac{1}{2} \frac{d}{ds}\left(\frac{a'(t)}{a^2(t)}\right) + \tfrac{1}{4}\left(\frac{a'(t)}{a^2(t)}\right)^2\right) v = 0. \tag{4.2}$$

Since

$$\int^s \frac{a'(t)}{a^2(t)} \, ds_1 = \int^s \frac{a'(t_1)}{a^2(t_1)} \frac{ds}{dt} \, dt_1$$

$$= \int^t \frac{a^t(t_1) \, dt_1}{a(t_1)} = \log a(t), \tag{4.3}$$

(1) reduces to

$$u = \frac{v}{a(t)^{1/2}}. \tag{4.4}$$

Hence we have reduced the original problem of obtaining approximate solutions of (1.1) to that of determining approximate solutions of equations of the form

$$v'' + (1 + b(s)) v = 0. \tag{4.5}$$

Under appropriate conditions on $a(t)$ as $t \to \infty$, we will have $b(s) \to 0$ as $s \to \infty$, and thus have the simple equation $v'' + v = 0$ as a comparison equation.

5. The Equation $u'' + (1 + b(t)) u = 0$

The study of the approximate solution for large t of the equation

$$u'' + (1 + b(t)) u = 0 \tag{5.1}$$

· where $b(t) \to 0$ as $t \to \infty$ proceeds by several stages. To begin with, we must study the boundedness of the solutions. There are many conditions upon $b(t)$ that ensure that all solutions of (5.1) are bounded as $t \to \infty$. The simplest and most important is the following:

THEOREM. If

$$\int^{\infty} |b(t)| \, dt < \infty, \tag{5.2}$$

then all solutions of (5.1) are bounded as $t \to \infty$.

As usual, the proof depends upon converting (5.1) into an appropriate integral equation. We write (5.1) in the form

$$u'' + u = -b(t) u, \tag{5.3}$$

and regard $-b(t) u$ as a forcing term. It follows that u can be taken as the solution of the linear integral equation

$$u = c_1 \cos t + c_2 \sin t + \int_0^t \sin(t - s) \, b(s) \, u(s) \, ds. \tag{5.4}$$

Hence, taking absolute values of both sides, we have the inequality

$$|u| \le |c_1| + |c_2| + \int_0^t |b(s)| \, |u(s)| \, ds. \tag{5.5}$$

It is remarkable that this inequality yields an upper bound for $|u(t)|$. This is a consequence of the following useful result.

LEMMA. If $u, v, c_3 \ge 0$, then the inequality

$$u(t) \le c_3 + \int_0^t v(s) \, u(s) \, ds \tag{5.6}$$

implies the inequality

$$u(t) \le c_3 \exp\left(\int_0^t v(s) \, ds\right). \tag{5.7}$$

The proof is simple. From (5.6) we have

$$\frac{u(t)}{c_3 + \int_0^t v(s) \, u(s) \, ds} \le 1. \tag{5.8}$$

Multiplying by $v(t)$ and integrating between 0 and t, we obtain

$$\log\left(c_3 + \int_0^t v(s) \, u(s) \, ds\right) - \log c_3 \le \int_0^t v(s) \, ds \tag{5.9}$$

or

$$c_3 + \int_0^t v(s) \, u(s) \, ds \le c_3 \exp\left(\int_0^t v(s) \, ds\right). \tag{5.10}$$

Referring to (5.6), we see that this yields (5.7). Using this result, (5.5) yields

$$| u | \le (| c_1 | + | c_2 |) \exp \left(\int_0^t | b(s) | \, ds \right)$$

$$\le (| c_1 | + | c_2 |) \exp \left(\int_0^\infty | b(s) | \, ds \right), \tag{5.11}$$

which establishes the stated result.

EXERCISES

5.1. Show that all solutions of

$$u'' + (1 + b(t))\, u = 0$$

are bounded it $b(t) \to 0$ and $\int^\infty | b'(t) | \, dt < \infty$.

5.2. If all solutions of

$$u'' + a(t)\, u = 0$$

belong to $L^2(0, \infty)$, then all solutions of

$$u'' + (a(t) + b(t))\, u = 0$$

belong to $L^2(0, \infty)$ if $| b(t) |$ is bounded for $t \ge 0$.

5.3. If all solutions of

$$u'' + a(t)\, u = 0$$

are bounded as $t \to \infty$, and $\int^\infty | b(t) | \, dt < \infty$, then all solutions of

$$u'' + (a(t) + b(t))\, u = 0$$

are bounded as $t \to \infty$.

5.4. Are all solutions of

$$u'' + \left(1 + \frac{\sin at}{t} \right) u = 0$$

bounded as $t \to \infty$?

5.5. For what values of a and b are all solutions of

$$u'' + \left(1 + \frac{\sin t^a}{t^b} \right) u = 0$$

bounded as $t \to \infty$?

5.6. To study the asymptotic behavior of

$$u'' + (1 + f(t)) u = 0,$$

let $v = u' + r(t) u$ where $r(t)$ is to be chosen judiciously. Obtain a second-order equation for v and let $r = 1 + f(t)/2$, to derive an asymptotic expression for $u(t)$ as $t \to \infty$. (This method is related to the classical *cascade method* of Laplace-Darboux used to study the equation

$$u_{xy} + au_x + bu_y + cu = 0.$$

See J. H. Billings, *Extensions of the Laplace Cascade Method*, Inst. for Fluid Dynamics, College Park, Maryland: University of Maryland Press, April, 1960.)

COMMENTS AND BIBLIOGRAPHY

This inequality was first developed and used for the study of the stability of the solutions of differential equations in

R. Bellman, "A Stability Property of Solutions of Linear Differential Equations," *Duke Math. J.*, **11**, 513-516, 1944.

Further results and references may be found in

R. Bellman, *Stability Theory of Differential Equations*, New York: McGraw-Hill Book Company, Inc., 1953,

where the results of the exercises are also discussed.

6. Asymptotic Behavior

Once we have established the boundedness of $|u(t)|$, it is easy to find an approximate expression for large t. Returning to (5.4), we have

$$u(t) = c_1 \cos t + c_2 \sin t + \sin t \int_0^t \cos s \, b(s) \, u(s) \, ds - \cos t \int_0^t \sin s \, b(s) \, u(s) \, ds.$$

$$(6.1)$$

Since $u(s)$ is bounded and $\int^\infty |b(s)| \, ds < \infty$, the integrals

$$a_1 = \int_0^\infty \cos s \, b(s) \, u(s) \, ds, \qquad a_2 = \int_0^\infty \sin s \, b(s) \, u(s) \, ds$$

are convergent. Hence

$$u(t) = c_1 \cos t + c_2 \sin t + a_1 \sin t - a_2 \cos t$$

$$- \sin t \int_t^\infty \cos s \, b(s) \, u(s) \, ds$$

$$- \cos t \int_t^\infty \sin s \, b(s) \, u(s) \, ds$$

$$= (c_1 + a_1) \cos t + (c_2 + a_2) \sin t + 0(1) \qquad (6.2)$$

as $t \to \infty$.

To obtain more precise results we iterate this process. We must impose further conditions upon $b(t)$, however, so that we can estimate the order of magnitude of the terms we obtain in this way.

EXERCISES

6.1. Consider the cases where $b(t) = 1/t$, $1/t^2$, e^{-t}.

6.2. Determine the asymptotic behavior of the solutions of $u'' + tu = 0$.

6.3. Consider the equation

$$u'' - (1 + b(t)) \, u = 0$$

where $\int^\infty |b(t)| \, dt < \infty$. Show that there are two particular solutions u_1 and u_2 with the respective asymptotic behaviors $u_1 \sim e^t$, $u_2 \sim e^{-t}$.

COMMENTS AND BIBLIOGRAPHY

The technique goes back to the beginnings of the modern theory of differential equations, having been extensively used by Liouville and Stekloff. See

G. Szegö, "Orthogonal Polynomials", *Am. Math. Soc. Colloq. Publ.*, Vol. XXIII, 1939.

where extensive applications are made and other references given, particularly on p. 204.

7. Statement of Results

Let us now put the preceding results together. The change of variable $s = \int_0^t a(t_1) \, dt_1$ converts the equation

$$u'' + a^2(t)u = 0 \qquad (7.1)$$

into the equation

$$\frac{d^2u}{ds^2} + \frac{a'(t)}{a^2(t)}\frac{du}{ds} + u = 0. \tag{7.2}$$

The change of dependent variable $u = v/a(t)^{1/2}$ converts this into the equation

$$v'' + \left(1 - \frac{1}{2}\frac{d}{ds}\left(\frac{a'(t)}{a^2(t)}\right) + \frac{1}{4}\left(\frac{a'(t)}{a^2(t)}\right)^2\right)v = 0. \tag{7.3}$$

If

$$\int^\infty \left|\frac{a'(t)}{a^2(t)}\right|^2 ds = \int^\infty \left|\frac{a'(t)}{a^2(t)}\right|^2 a(t)\,dt < \infty,$$

$$\int^\infty \left|\frac{d}{ds}\left(\frac{a'(t)}{a^2(t)}\right)\right| ds = \int^\infty \left|\frac{d}{ds}\left(\frac{a'(t)}{a^2(t)}\right)\right| dt < \infty, \tag{7.4}$$

we know from the theorem of Section 5 that every solution of (7.3) has the asymptotic form

$$v = c_1 \cos s + c_2 \sin s + o(1). \tag{7.5}$$

Hence

THEOREM.   If $a(t) > 0$, for $t \ge t_0$ and

$$\int^\infty \frac{a'(t)^2}{a^3(t)}\,dt < \infty, \qquad \int^\infty \left|\frac{d}{dt}\left(\frac{a'(t)}{a^2(t)}\right)\right| dt < \infty, \tag{7.6}$$

then all solutions of

$$u'' + a^2(t)\,u = 0 \tag{7.7}$$

have the form

$$u = \frac{c_1 \cos\left(\int_0^t a(t_1)\,dt_1\right) + c_2 \sin\left(\int_0^t a(t_1)\,dt_1\right)}{\sqrt{a(t)}} + o\left(\frac{1}{\sqrt{a(t)}}\right) \tag{7.8}$$

as $t \to \infty$.

EXERCISES

7.1. Apply the foregoing results to the equations

$$u'' + t^2 u = 0, \qquad u'' + e^{2t}u = 0.$$

7.2. Under what conditions upon $b(t)$ and $b'(t)$ can we conclude that the solutions of

$$u'' + (1 + b(t))\,u = 0$$

have the asymptotic form

$$u = c_1 \cos t + c_2 \sin t + o(1)$$

as $t \to \infty$?

7.3. Determine the asymptotic behavior of solutions of $u'' + u/t = 0$ by applying the Liouville transformation repeatedly.

7.4. Consider the equation $u'' + q(t) u = 0$, and make the simultaneous change of dependent and independent variable $v = u'$, $ds = q(t) dt$. Show that

$$\frac{d^2v}{ds^2} + \frac{v}{q(t)} = 0$$

and thus consider the connection between the behavior of the solutions of $u'' + a^2(t) u = 0$ as $a(t) \to 0$ and as $a(t) \to \infty$. (See P. Hartman, *On the Existence of Large and Small Solutions of Linear Differential Equations*, Technical Note No. 20, Baltimore: Johns Hopkins University Press, 1960 and A. Wintner, "On a Principle of Reciprocity Between High- and Low-frequency Problems," *Q. Appl. Math.*, **15**, 314-317, 1957.)

8. Asymptotic Form

Consider the equation

$$u'' + (1 + b(t)) u = 0, \qquad u(a) = c_1, \qquad u'(a) = c_2, \tag{8.1}$$

under the assumption that $\int^\infty | b(t) | \, dt < \infty$. From what has preceded, we know that u has the asymptotic form

$$u \sim b_1 e^{it} + b_2 e^{-it} \tag{8.2}$$

as $t \to \infty$. In many important physical applications, only the parameters b_1 and b_2 are of interest, the asymptotic phase shift caused by the inhomogeneity expressed by $b(t)$. It is clear that b_1 and b_2 are functions of the initial point a, but it is not easy to say more. What can we deduce concerning the nature of these functions?

A certain amount of information can be obtained by means of the functional equation approach applied earlier in Chapters One and Two, compare Section 24. Starting with the relation

$$u(t) \sim e^{it}(c_1 f_{11}(a) + c_2 f_{12}(a)) + e^{-it}(c_1 f_{21}(a) + c_2 f_2(a)), \tag{8.3}$$

(since we know that b_1 and b_2 depend linearly upon the initial values c_1 and c_2), we have immediately

$$u(t + \Delta) \sim e^{i(t+\Delta)} (c_1 f_{11}(a) + c_2 f_{12}(a))$$
$$+ e^{-i(t+\Delta)} (c_1 f_{21}(a) + c_2 f_{22}(a)), \qquad (8.4)$$

and also, using (8.3) starting from the point $t + \Delta$,

$$u(t + \Delta) \sim e^{it} ((c_1 + c_2\Delta) f_{11}(a + \Delta)$$
$$+ (c_2 - (1 + b(a) c_1) \Delta) f_{12}(a + \Delta))$$
$$+ e^{-it} ((c_1 + c_2\Delta) f_{21}(a + \Delta)$$
$$+ (c_2 - (1 + f(a)) c_1) \Delta) f_{22}(a + \Delta)), \qquad (8.5)$$

to terms in $o(\Delta)$. Expanding the functions of a and letting $\Delta \to 0$, we obtain a system of linear equations for the functions $f_{ij}(a)$.

It is clear that we will obtain a firmer comprehension of the structure of this system if we use vector-matrix notation. In place of (8.1), write

$$x' = B(t) x, \qquad x(a) = c, \qquad (8.6)$$

where

$$x = \begin{pmatrix} u \\ u' \end{pmatrix}, \qquad B(t) = \begin{pmatrix} 0 & 1 \\ -(1 + b(t)) & 0 \end{pmatrix}. \qquad (8.7)$$

In place of (8.2), we write

$$u(t) \sim (F(a) c, y(t)), \qquad (8.8)$$

an inner product, where

$$y(t) = \begin{pmatrix} e^{it} \\ e^{-it} \end{pmatrix}, \qquad F(a) = (f_{ij}(a)), \qquad i, j = 1, 2. \qquad (8.9)$$

We then have, corresponding to (8.4) and (8.5), the two relations

$$u(t + \Delta) \sim (F(a) c, y(t + \Delta))$$
$$\sim (F(a + \Delta) (I + B(a) \Delta) c, y(t)). \qquad (8.10)$$

Since, to terms in $0(\Delta)$,

$$y(t + \Delta) = \begin{pmatrix} e^{it}(1 + i\Delta) \\ e^{-it}(1 - i\Delta) \end{pmatrix} = \begin{pmatrix} 1 + i\Delta & 0 \\ 0 & 1 - i\Delta \end{pmatrix} y(t) = (I + C\Delta) y(t), \quad (8.11)$$

equating coefficients of $c_1 e^{it}$, $c_1 e^{-it}$, $c_2 e^{it}$, $c_2 e^{-it}$, and letting $\Delta \to 0$ in (8.10) yields the equation

$$F'(a) + F(a) B(a) = CF(a). \qquad (8.12)$$

Setting $F(a) = e^{Ca}G(a)$, we see that $G(a)$ satisfies the equation

$$G'(a) + G(a) B(a) = 0, \tag{8.13}$$

the adjoint of the matrix version of (8.6).

Having come so far, we face the difficulty that we do not possess any initial values for the solution of (8.13). We now know something of the structure of the parameters b_1 and b_2 in (8.2), but they are not completely determined. In following sections we will apply the method to some specific equations.

COMMENTS AND BIBLIOGRAPHY

A number of ingenious techniques have been devised to obtain numerical estimates of $F(0)$, notably the variational methods originating in the work of Schwinger. See

B. A. Lippman and J. Schwinger, *Phys. Rev.*, **79**, 469, 1950.

the paper by S. Altschuler referred to earlier, and

F. Calogero, "Analytic Continuation and Asymptotic Behavior in Angular Momentum of the Scattering Matrix in Potential Scattering," *Nuovo Cimento*, to appear.

See also,

I. I. Kolodner, "Phase Shift of Solutions of Second Order Linear Ordinary Differential Equations and Related Problems," *J. Math. Analysis and Appl.*, **4**, 422-439, 1962.

For applications of the theory of invariant imbedding, see

C. J. MacCallum, *Invariant Imbedding and Wave Propagation in Inhomogeneous Media*, Albuquerque, New Mexico: Sandia Corporation, November, 1961.

The inverse problem of determining the coefficient matrix $B(t)$ from the asymptotic behavior of $x(t)$ is one of importance in quantum theory. See

I. M. Gelfand and B. M. Levitan, "On the Determination of a Differential Equation from its Spectral Function," *Trans. Amer. Math. Soc.*, **2**, 253-304, 1955.

M. Verde, "The Inversion Problem in Wave Mechanics and Dispersion Relations," *Nuclear Physics*, **9**, 255-266, 1958-1959.

For a treatment of the problem of determining the function $\phi(t)$ from a knowledge of the characteristic values of the equation

$$u'' + \lambda\phi(t) u = 0, \qquad u(0) + a_1 u'(0) = 0,$$
$$u(1) + a_1 u'(1) \doteq 0,$$

see

G. Borg, "Eine Umkehrung der Sturm-Liouvilleschen Eigenwertaufgabe. Bestimmung der differential Gleichung durch die Eigenwerte," *Acta Math.*, **78**, 1-96, 1946.

where reference to earlier work by Ambarzumian and Langer is given.

9. $u'' - \left(1 + \sum_{k=1}^{R} z_k e^{-\lambda_k t}\right) u = 0$

As an example of an application of the foregoing technique to an equation of special type where we can carry the analysis a few steps further, consider the equation

$$u'' - (1 + ze^{-\lambda t}) u = 0, \qquad u(0) = c_1, \qquad u'(0) = c_2, \qquad (9.1)$$

where $\mathrm{Re}\,(\lambda) > 0$.

On the basis of a general result which we mentioned earlier, (Section 6, Exercise 3) we know that

$$\lim_{t \to \infty} u(t)\, e^{-t} = f(c_1, c_2, z) \qquad (9.2)$$

exists. It follows as above that f is linear in c_1 and c_2, having the form

$$f(c_1, c_2, z) = c_1 f_1(z) + c_2 f_2(z). \qquad (9.3)$$

We wish to obtain equations determining $f_1(z)$ and $f_2(z)$. The effect of replacing t by $t + \Delta$, Δ an infinitesimal, is to convert the equation of (9.1) into

$$u'' - (1 + ze^{-\lambda\Delta}e^{-\lambda t}) u = 0. \qquad (9.4)$$

Simultaneously the initial conditions are transformed into

$$u(0) = c_1 + c_2\Delta, \qquad u'(0) = c_2 + \Delta(1 + z)\,c_1, \qquad (9.5)$$

to terms in $o(\Delta)$. Hence, from the definition of f_1 and f_2 we obtain the relations

$$c_1 f_1(z) + c_2 f_2(z) = \lim_{t \to \infty} u(t)\, e^{-t}$$

$$= \lim_{t \to \infty} u(t + \Delta)\, e^{-(t+\Delta)}$$

$$= e^{-\Delta} \lim_{t \to \infty} u(t + \Delta)\, e^{-t}$$

$$= e^{-\Delta}[(c_1 + c_2\Delta)\, f_1(ze^{-\lambda\Delta}) + (c_2 + \Delta(1 + z)\, c_1)\, f_2(ze^{-\lambda\Delta})].$$

$$(9.6)$$

Expanding in powers of Δ and equating coefficients, we obtain the system of simultaneous equations

$$zf_1' = \frac{(1+z)f_2 - f_1}{\lambda},$$

$$zf_2' = \frac{f_1 - f_2}{\lambda}. \tag{9.7}$$

The initial conditions are now readily obtained. When $z = 0$, the exact solution of (9.1) is

$$u = \left(\frac{c_1 + c_2}{2}\right) e^t + \left(\frac{c_1 - c_2}{2}\right) e^{-t}. \tag{9.8}$$

Hence $f_1(0) = f_2(0) = \frac{1}{2}$.

Writing

$$f_1(z) = \sum_{n=0}^{\infty} a_n z^n, \qquad f_2(z) = \sum_{n=0}^{\infty} b_n z^n, \tag{9.9}$$

we readily obtain recurrence relations

$$na_n = \frac{b_n - a_n}{\lambda} + \frac{b_{n-1}}{\lambda},$$

$$nb_n = \frac{a_n - b_n}{\lambda}. \tag{9.10}$$

The determinant is $n(n + 2/\lambda)$, which means that a_n and b_n can be determined recursively if $\mathrm{Re}\,(\lambda) > 0$.

EXERCISES

9.1. Show that $f_1(z)$ and $f_2(z)$ are entire function of z.

9.2. Extend the foregoing results to cover the equation

$$u'' - \left(1 + \sum_{k=1}^{R} z_k e^{-\lambda_k t}\right) u = 0.$$

9.3. Consider the matrix equation

$$x' - (A + e^{-Bt}z) x = 0$$

using the same ideas.

9.4. Consider

$$u'' - (1 + ze^{-t^2+wt})\, u = 0$$

writing

$$\lim_{t\to\infty} e^{-t}u = f_1(z, w)\, c_1 + f_2(z, w)\, c_2 .$$

9.5. Consider

$$u'' - (1 + b(t + z))\, u = 0,$$

writing

$$\lim_{t\to\infty} e^{-t}u = f_1(z)\, c_1 + f_2(z)\, c_2 .$$

(For the foregoing results, see R. Bellman, "On Asymptotic Behavior of Solutions of Second Order Differential Equations," *Q. Appl. Math.*, **20**, 385-387, 1963.)

9.6. Use similar techniques to obtain an equation for $f(c_1, c_2, a)$, the first zero of $u'' - g(t)\, u = 0$, $u(a) = c_1$, $u'(a) = c_2$.

10. WKB Approximation

Let us now consider one of the most useful and important approximation techniques in mathematical physics, a technique developed independently by Wentzel, Kramers and Brillouin and called therefore the WKB approximation. As usual, the attribution is not completely accurate, since many others attained the same result independently, and earlier, notably Liouville, Green, Jeffreys, and Blumenthal.

In place of considering the behavior of the solutions as $t \to \infty$, let us keep the t-interval finite and consider the behavior of the solution as a parameter in the equation increases without limit. Let

$$u'' + \lambda^2 a^2(t)\, u = 0 \qquad (10.1)$$

where $a(t)$ is uniformly bounded and positive in $0 \le t \le 1$ and λ is a large constant. Then the Liouville change of variable

$$s = \lambda \int_0^t a(t_1)\, dt_1 \qquad (10.2)$$

converting (10.1) into

$$\frac{d^2v}{ds^2} + \frac{a'(t)}{\lambda a^2(t)} \frac{du}{ds} + u = 0, \qquad (10.3)$$

and eliminating the middle term (compare § 3), takes this into

$$v'' + \left(1 - \frac{1}{2\lambda} \frac{d}{ds} \left(\frac{a'(t)}{a^2(t)}\right) + \frac{1}{4\lambda^2} \left(\frac{a'(t)}{a^2(t)}\right)^2\right) v = 0. \tag{10.4}$$

Hence, if $\lambda \gg 1$ an excellent approximation to (10.1) is furnished by the expression

$$u = \frac{\exp\left(\pm i\lambda \int_0^t a(t_1)\, dt_1\right)}{\lambda a(t)^{1/2}}. \tag{10.5}$$

Provided that $a(t) \geq b > 0$ in $[0, 1]$, as we hypothesized, and that $|a'(t)|$ and $|a''(t)|$ are bounded, the functions occurring in (10.4) are integrable over $[0, 1]$.

EXERCISES

10.1. Use the perturbation techniques of Chapter One to obtain a solution of (10.4) of the form

$$v = \cos s + \frac{v_1(s)}{\lambda} + \frac{v_2(s)}{\lambda^2} + \cdots.$$

COMMENTS AND BIBLIOGRAPHY

The approximation embodied in the foregoing analysis dates back to the beginning of the modern theory of differential equations; see

G. Green, "On the Motion of Waves in a Variable Canal of Small Depth and Width," *Trans. Cambridge Phil. Soc.*, **6**, 457-462, 1837.

L. Liouville, "Sur le developpement des fonctions ou parties de fonctions en series," *J. Math. Pures Appl.*, **2**, 16-35, 1837.

References to the papers of Brillouin, Blumenthal, Jeffreys, Kramers, and Wentzel may be found in

F. W. J. Olver, "Error Bounds for the Liouville-Green (or WKB) Approximation," *Proc. Cambridge Phil. Soc.*, **57**, 790-810, 1961.

See

V. B. Uvarov and A. F. Nikiforov, "On an Approximation Method for the Solution of the Schrodinger Equation," *Zh. vychisl. matem. i matem. fiz.*, **1**, 177-179, 1961,

for an important technique that we have not discussed here.

For a general discussion of classical mechanics as a limiting form of quantum mechanics, see

V. P. Maslov, "The Quasi-classical Asymptotic Solutions of Some Problems in Mathematical Physics," *USSR Computational Math. and Math. Physics*, Pergamon Press, No. 1, 123-141, 1962.

11. Riccati Equation

A very convenient way to obtain the asymptotic behavior of the solution of

$$u'' - a^2(t)\,u = 0, \qquad (11.1)$$

as $t \to \infty$ and indeed more precise asymptotic behavior, is to employ the associated Riccati equation,

$$v' + v^2 - a^2(t) = 0, \qquad (11.2)$$

obtained by setting $v = u'/u$, or $u = \exp\left(\int_0^t v\,dt_1\right)$.

Suppose that $a(t) \to \infty$ in such a way that $a'(t)/a(t) \to 0$. Referring to (11.2), we look for a solution of the form

$$v = a(t) + w, \qquad (11.3)$$

where $w/a(t) \to 0$ as $t \to \infty$. Substituting in (11.2), we have

$$w' + a'(t) + w^2 + 2a(t)\,w = 0. \qquad (11.4)$$

It is reasonable to expect that $w'/w \to 0$ as $t \to \infty$, and by assumption $w^2/a(t)\,w \to 0$ as $t \to \infty$. Hence, if (11.4) is to hold, we may expect to have

$$2a(t)\,w + a'(t) \to 0, \qquad (11.5)$$

as $t \to \infty$, whence $w \cong -\,a'(t)/2a(t)$. This yields, once again, the WKB approximation.

It is clear that we can continue in this fashion, obtaining more and more accurate estimates for v, provided that we impose further conditions upon $a(t)$ and its derivatives.

EXERCISES

11.1. Obtain an asymptotic series expansion for the solution of

$$u'' + \frac{a^2(t)}{h^2}\,u = 0$$

having the form

$$u = \frac{\exp\left(\frac{i}{h}\int_0^t a(s)\,ds\right)}{a(t)^{1/2}}\,[1 + b_1(t)\,h + b_2(t)\,h^2 + \cdots]$$

using the Riccati equation

$$v' + v^2 + \frac{a^2(t)}{h^2} = 0,$$

where $v = u'/u$. (In quantum mechanics, $\lambda = 1/h$, where h is Planck's constant.)

11.2. Similarly, obtain an asymptotic series expansion for the solutions of

$$u'' + \left(\frac{a^2(t)}{h^2} + b(t)\right)u = 0.$$

11.3. Show that $-v^2 = \min_{w}\,[w^2 - 2wv]$.

11.4. Hence show that the equation in (11.2) may be written

$$v' = \min_{w}\,[w^2 - 2wv + a^2(t)].$$

Let $V(w, t)$ represent the solution of

$$V' = w^2 - 2wV + a^2(t),\quad V(0) = v(0).$$

Show that $v = \min_{w} V$.

(This is an application of the theory of quasilinearization.

See

R. Bellman, "Functional Equations in the Theory of Dynamic Programming—V: Positivity and Quasi-linearity," *Proc. Nat. Acad. Sci. USA*, **41**, 743-746, 1955.

R. Bellman, "A Note on Asymptotic Behavior of Differential Equations," *Boll. d'Unione Mate.*, **18**, 16-18, 1963.

F. Calogero, "A Variational Principle for Scattering Phase Shifts," *Nuovo Cimento*, to appear in 1963.)

R. Kalaba, "On Nonlinear Differential Equations, the Maximum Operation, and Monotone Convergence," *J. Math. and Mech.*, **8**, 519-574, 1959.

COMMENTS AND BIBLIOGRAPHY

The equation $u' = a + bu + cu^2 + du^3$ has been treated in great detail by Liouville. See

J. Liouville, *Acta Math.*, **27**, 55-78, 1903.

12. Langer Approximation

Returning to the equation

$$u'' + \lambda^2 a^2(t)\, u = 0, \tag{12.1}$$

we see that our fundamental device has been to introduce a comparison equation whose solution is completely determined. This is the basic idea that can be utilized in situations where the Liouville-transformation is not applicable.

Consider, for example, the equation

$$u'' + \lambda(t - \tfrac{1}{2})\, b(t)\, u = 0, \tag{12.2}$$

where $b(t) \geq b > 0$ in $[0, 1]$ and λ is a large parameter. For $0 \leq t \leq \tfrac{1}{2} - \delta$, we can apply the previous methods. We cannot apply a single substitution over the entire interval because of the change of sign of $t - \tfrac{1}{2}$.

Writing this equation in the form

$$u'' + \lambda(t - \tfrac{1}{2})\, [b_0 + b_1(t - \tfrac{1}{2}) + \cdots]\, u = 0, \tag{12.3}$$

we suspect that in the neighborhood of $t = \tfrac{1}{2}$, the solution behaves like the solution of the comparison equation

$$u'' + \lambda(t - \tfrac{1}{2})\, b_0 u = 0. \tag{12.4}$$

This is indeed the case, and this technique of Langer plays an important role in quantum mechanics. There is considerable difficulty in fitting the three approximate solutions together and we shall therefore refer to the literature for further details.

COMMENTS AND BIBLIOGRAPHY

The basic papers were by R. Langer. The most recent results and references may be found in

A. Erdelyi, *Asymptotic Expansions*, Dover Publications, New York, 1956.

———, "Asymptotic Solutions of Differential Equations with Transition Points or Singularities," *J. Math. and Phys.*, 1, 16-28, 1960.

See also

V. B. Uvarov and V. B. Nikiforov, "On an Approximate Method for the Solution of the Schrödinger Equation," *Referativnyy, Zhurnal, Matematika*, No. 3, 1962, 30, 3V161 (*Zh. vychisl. matem. i matem. fiz.*, no. 1, 1, 177-179, 1961.)

13. Wave Propagation and the WKB Approximation

So far the WKB approximation has been derived as the consequence of an analytic device. Let us now show that it has a very simple physical interpretation. The importance of this interpretation is twofold. In the first place, it enables us to obtain higher-order approximations in a meaningful fashion; in the second place it enables us to obtain corresponding approximations for more complex functional equations where the analytic transformations are not apparent.

The key observation is that the equation

$$u'' + k^2(x)\, u = 0 \tag{13.1}$$

arises from the study of one-dimensional wave motion. Let us begin with the equation

$$\frac{\partial^2 u}{\partial x^2} - a^2 \frac{\partial^2 u}{\partial t^2} = 0, \tag{13.2}$$

assumed to hold for $-\infty < x < \infty$, $-\infty < t < \infty$. If we look for solutions that are periodic in t, of the form $u(x, t) = u(x)\, e^{i\omega t}$, where ω is a real constant, we find that $u(x)$ satisfies the ordinary differential equation

$$u''(x) + a^2\omega^2 u = 0. \tag{13.3}$$

We obtain the two solutions

$$u = b_1 e^{ia\omega x} + b_2 e^{-ia\omega x}. \tag{13.4}$$

The particular solution $e^{ia\omega x}$ represents a wave propagated to the right and $e^{-ia\omega x}$ a wave propagated to the left. We may thus consider (13.1) to arise from the study of wave propagation through an inhomogeneous medium; that is, a^2 depends upon x.

Let us now consider the solution of (13.1) in the case where $k^2(x)$ has the form

$$k^2(x) = k_1^2, \qquad -\infty < x \le y,$$
$$= k^2(x), \qquad y < x < \infty. \tag{13.5}$$

We may then consider the problem of solving (13.1) as equivalent to that of determining the reflection and transmission of a wave starting in $[-\infty, y]$ by an inhomogeneous region, starting at $x = y$.

To tackle this problem, we study first the problem of the reflection of a plane wave by a homogeneous semi-infinite medium. Mathematically, this is the problem of determining the solution of the system of second-order linear differential equations

$$u'' + k_1^2 u = 0, \qquad -\infty < x < y,$$

$$u'' + k_2^2 u = 0, \qquad y < x < \infty, \tag{13.6}$$

where k_1 and k_2 are positive constants, $k_1 \neq k_2$, $u(x)$ and $u'(x)$ are assumed to be continuous at $x = y$, and we look for solutions of the form

$$u = e^{ik_1 x} + re^{-ik_1 x}, \qquad x < y,$$

$$= te^{ik_2 x}, \qquad x > y. \tag{13.7}$$

We think of $e^{ik_1 x}$ (Fig. 5) as an incoming wave, starting from $-\infty$ and impinging upon the semi-infinite interval (y, ∞).

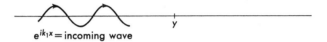

$e^{ik_1 x} =$ incoming wave

Fig. 5.

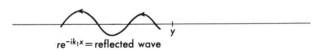

$re^{-ik_1 x} =$ reflected wave

Fig. 6.

The term $re^{-ik_1 x}$ (Fig. 6) represents, in this framework, the reflected wave, with the complex quantity r representing the amplitude and phase of the reflected wave. Similarly $te^{ik_2 x}$ (Fig. 7) represents a transmitted wave moving to the right.

$te^{ik_2 x} =$ transmitted wave

Fig. 7.

To simplify the determination of the quantities r and t, let us normalize by writing the solutions in the form

$$u = e^{ik_1(x-y)} + re^{-ik_1(x-y)}, \qquad -\infty < x < y,$$

$$= te^{ik_2(x-y)}, \qquad \infty > x > y. \tag{13.8}$$

Matching the values of u and u' at $x = y$, we obtain the relations

$$1 + r = t,$$
$$ik_1 - ik_2 r = ik_2 t, \qquad (13.9)$$

which yields the values

$$t = \frac{2k_1}{k_1 + k_2},$$

$$r = \frac{k_1 - k_2}{k_1 + k_2}. \qquad (13.10)$$

We see that the intensity of the reflected wave depends upon the difference between k_1 and k_2.

We can now consider the situation where k_2 is not constant as given by (12.5). We consider the inhomogeneous region to consist of a sequence of homogeneous strata, $[y, y + \Delta]$, $[y + \Delta, y + 2\Delta]$, $\cdots$, as indicated below.

The incoming wave suffers a reflection and transmission at the interface $x = y$. The process is repeated at $x = y + \Delta$, $x = y + 2\Delta$, and so on. Suppose that we keep track only of the transmitted wave at each interface, paying no attention to reflections. Then, using the relation in (13.10) repeatedly we see that the disturbance at x is given by

$$I(x) = \left(\frac{2k(y)}{k(y) + k(y + \Delta)} e^{ik(y)\Delta} \right) \left(\frac{2k(y + \Delta)}{k(y + \Delta) + k(y + 2\Delta)} e^{ik(y+\Delta)\Delta} \right) \cdots. \qquad (13.11)$$

Passing to the limit as $\Delta \to 0$, we obtain after some simple manipulations

$$I(x) = \frac{\exp\left(i \int_0^x k(y)\, dy \right)}{k(x)^{1/2}}, \qquad (13.12)$$

the WKB approximation.

EXERCISES

13.1. Taking account of waves reflected twice only, find the first correction term to (13.12).

13.2. Adding up double reflections, quadruple reflections and so on, obtain the solution of $u'' + k^2(x)\, u = 0$ at a point $x > y$ in the form of an infinite series (the Bremmer series).

COMMENTS AND BIBLIOGRAPHY

The fact that the WKB approximation can be obtained in the foregoing fashion appears to have been common knowledge for some time, and it is not clear as to who first used this very elegant technique. The representation of $u(x)$ as a series as suggested by Exercise 13.2 appears first to have been given by Bremmer, see

H. Bremmer, "The WKB Approximation as the First Term of a Geometric-optical Series," *Theory of Electromagnetic Waves*, Interscience, 125-138, 1951.

The convergence of the series was discussed by Bellman and Kalaba in

R. Bellman and R. Kalaba, "Functional Equations, Wave Propagation and Invariant Imbedding," *J. Math. and Mech.*, **8**, 683-704, 1959,

and the concept of successive reflections and transmissions was combined with the theory of invariant imbedding to provide a new foundation for the theory of wave propagation; see also

R. Bellman and R. Kalaba, "Wave Branching Processes and Invariant Imbedding—I," *Proc. Nat. Acad. Sci. US*, **47**, 1507-1509, 1961.

The precise conditions of convergence of the Bremmer series were given by Atkinson,

F. V. Atkinson, "Wave Propagation and the Bremmer Series," *J. Math. Analysis and Appl.*, **1**, 255-276, 1960.

who showed that it was the Liouville-Neumann series of the solution of an appropriate integral equation. It was then shown by Kay and Keller-Keller that a slightly modified integral equation, of Volterra type, could be used possessing the advantage that the corresponding series converge for all $k(x)$ with the property that $k(x) \geq a^2 > 0$, $\int^x |k'(y)| \, dy < \infty$ for $z > y$. See

H. B. Keller and J. B. Keller, "Exponential-like Solutions of Systems of Linear Ordinary Differential Equations," *J. Soc. Ind. Appl. Math.*, **10**, 246-259, 1962.

The technique given here can be extended to treat vector-matrix systems of the form

$$x'' + A^2(t)\, x = 0,$$

(see Bellman-Kalaba cited above), and to obtain the analogue of the WKB approximations for partial differential equations and more general functional equations. These analogues can be obtained from the integral equations of Atkinson, Kay, or directly by means of the "principle of localization" used in the works of Bellman and Kalaba.

For a detailed application of invariant imbedding techniques to problems of the foregoing type, with numerous applications to modern physics, see

C. J. MacCallum, *Invariant Imbedding and Wave Propagation in Inhomogeneous Media*, Albuquerque, New Mexico: Sandia Corporation, November, 1961.

14. $u'' - (1 + t^{-2}) u = 0$

We have indicated in previous sections that the equation

$$u'' - (1 + f(t)) u = 0 \tag{14.1}$$

has two solutions, u_1 and u_2, with the respective properties

$$u_1 \sim e^t, \qquad u_2 \sim e^{-t} \tag{14.2}$$

as $t \to \infty$, provided that

$$\int^\infty | f(t) | \, dt < \infty. \tag{14.3}$$

If we take $f(t)$ to be the function $1/t^2$, how much more information can we extract from (14.1) concerning the asymptotic behavior of solutions of (14.1) as $t \to \infty$?

Writing the equation in the form

$$u'' - u = \frac{u}{t^2}, \tag{14.4}$$

we convert it, in the usual way, into the linear integral equation

$$u = c_1 e^t + c_2 e^{-t} + \int_1^t \left[\frac{e^{(t-s)} - e^{-(t-s)}}{2} \right] \frac{u(s) \, ds}{s^2}. \tag{14.5}$$

This, in turn, is written

$$u = e^t \left(c_1 + \int_1^\infty \frac{e^{-s} u(s) \, ds}{s^2} \right) - e^t \int_t^\infty \frac{e^{-s} u(s) \, ds}{s^2} - e^{-t} \int_1^t \frac{e^s u(s) \, ds}{s^2}. \tag{14.6}$$

Since all solutions of (14.1) are $0(e^t)$ as $t \to \infty$, the foregoing infinite integrals converge. To improve the estimate of (14.2), let us assume for the moment that

$$c_3 = c_1 + \int_1^\infty \frac{e^{-s} u(s) \, ds}{s^2} \neq 0. \tag{14.7}$$

Subsequently we shall discuss how this may be ensured. The second term in (14.6) has the bound

$$\left| e^{-t} \int_t^\infty \frac{e^{-s} u(s) \, ds}{s^2} \right| = 0 \left(e^t \int_t^\infty \frac{e^{-s} e^s \, ds}{s^2} \right) = 0 \left(\frac{e^t}{t} \right) \tag{14.8}$$

as $t \to \infty$. The third term is bounded by

$$\left| e^{-t} \int_1^{t/2} + e^{-t} \int_{t/2}^t \right| = 0\left(e^{-t}\, e^{3t/2} \int_1^{t/2} \frac{ds}{s^2} + e^t \int_{t/2}^t \frac{ds}{s^2} \right) = 0\left(\frac{e^t}{t} \right). \qquad (14.9)$$

Hence we may write

$$u = c_3 e^t + 0\left(\frac{e^t}{t} \right). \qquad (14.10)$$

This, in turn, when substituted in (14.6), will yield

$$u = c_3 e^t + \frac{c_4 e^t}{t} + 0\left(\frac{e^t}{t^2} \right). \qquad (14.11)$$

Inductively, we obtain an expression of the form

$$u = c_3 e^t + c_4 \frac{e^t}{t} + \cdots + 0\left(\frac{e^t}{t^N} \right) \qquad (14.12)$$

for any $N \geq 1$.

To ensure the nonvanishing of c_3, we start not at $t = 1$, but at $t = t_0$ where t_0 is sufficiently large. Then, in place of (14.7), we have

$$c_3 = c_1 + \int_{t_0}^{\infty} \frac{e^{-s}\, u(s)\, ds}{s^2} \qquad (14.13)$$

and it is easy to see from the nature of the bound on $|\, u(t)\,|$ that the integral term cannot cancel c_1 if $c_1 \neq 0$ and t_0 is taken large enough.

15. Discussion

Having obtained the series of approximations of (14.12), a number of questions irresistibly bubble to the surface:

1. Does the infinite series

$$S(t) = e^t \left(c_3 + \frac{c_4}{t} + \cdots \right)$$

converge? If not, what information can be gleaned from it concerning the solutions of (14.4)?

2. Can we determine the sequence of coefficients, $[c_3, c_4, \cdots]$, in some more convenient fashion?

3. How do we find a corresponding expression for the solution asymptotic to e^{-t} as $t \to \infty$?

We shall direct our attention to the second and third questions first and then turn to the first question.

16. Determination of Coefficients

Once we suspect the existence of a formal solution of (14.4) of the form

$$u = e^t \left(1 + \frac{b_1}{t} + \frac{b_2}{t^2} + \cdots + \frac{b_n}{t^n} + \cdots\right) \tag{16.1}$$

it is natural to attempt to evaluate the coefficients by means of direct substitution in (14.4) and equating of coefficients. This can be done without difficulty. We have

$$e^t \left(\sum_{n=1}^{\infty} \frac{b_n}{t^n}\right) - 2e^t \left(\sum_{n=1}^{\infty} \frac{nb_n}{t^{n+1}}\right) + e^t \left(\sum_{n=1}^{\infty} \frac{n(n+1)b_n}{t^{n+2}}\right)$$

$$- e^t \left(\sum_{n=1}^{\infty} \frac{b_n}{t^n}\right) - e^t \left(\sum_{n=1}^{\infty} \frac{b_n}{t^{n+2}}\right) = 0. \tag{16.2}$$

Hence we obtain the recurrence relation

$$2nb_n = ((n+1)(n+2) - 1)b_{n-1} \tag{16.3}$$

or

$$b_n = \left(\frac{n^2 + 3n + 1}{2n}\right) b_{n-1}.$$

It follows from this that the series in (16.1) diverges for all finite values of t! If the linear differential equation had the form

$$u'' - \left(1 + \frac{1}{t^2} + \frac{1}{t^3}\right) u = 0, \tag{16.4}$$

we would not obtain a simple recurrence relation of the foregoing type, but rather one involving b_n, b_{n-1}, and b_{n-2}. In any case, it is clear that the sequence of coefficients can be computed recurrently, so that there is no difficulty involved in a *formal* determination of the series.

EXERCISES

16.1. Set $u'/u = v$ and determine the formal series expansion for v, and thence for u, by means of the first order equation

$$v' + v^2 - 1 - \frac{1}{t^2} = 0.$$

For other approaches, see the papers by Calogero referred to earlier in Chapter 1, and

R. Bellman, "A Note on Asymptotic Behavior," *Boll. d'Unione Mate.*, to appear in 1963.

16.2. Find a formal series expansion for the solution of

$$v' + v^2 - 1 - \frac{1}{t} = 0.$$

16.3. Find a second-order linear differential equation with rational coefficients satisfied by the formal series $\sum_{n=1}^{\infty} n!/t^n$, divergent for all finite t.

17. The Second Solution—I

There are always special methods available for the treatment of the second-order equation that are not available for the general equation of nth order. Thus, to obtain the asymptotic solution of the solution of

$$u'' - (1 + f(t)) u = 0 \tag{17.1}$$

asymptotic to e^{-t} we can use the Riccati equation of the foregoing set of exercises, starting with the approximation $v = -1$. We leave this as an exercise for the reader. Or, we may use the relation connecting any two solutions

$$u_1 u_2' - u_1' u_2 = c_1, \tag{17.2}$$

where c_1 is a constant, to show that

$$u_2 = u_1 \int_t^\infty \frac{dt}{u_1^2} \tag{17.3}$$

is a solution of (17.1), provided that the infinite integral converges. We leave the verification of this, together with its use to derive the asymptotic behavior of u_2, as a further exercise for the reader.

18. The Second Solution—II

Let us now present a method that can be used to study the general nth order linear differential equation. Returning to (14.5), we want to single out the solution which behaves like e^{-t} as $t \to \infty$. Let us then write the integral equation in the form

$$u = c_2 e^{-t} + e^t \int_t^\infty \frac{e^{-s} u(s) \, ds}{s^2} - e^{-t} \int_t^\infty \frac{e^s u(s) \, ds}{s^2} , \tag{18.1}$$

upon suitably adding multiples of e^{-t} and e^t.

We leave as an exercise for the reader the task of carrying out the estimations corresponding to those of Section 14 and thus of establishing the existence of a solution of the form

$$u = e^{-t} \left[c_2 + \frac{c_3}{t} + \cdots + \frac{c_n}{t^n} + \cdots \right] \tag{18.2}$$

as $t \to \infty$.

19. Asymptotic Series

We have seen in the foregoing sections that formal series of the type

$$u = \left[c_0 + \frac{c_1}{t} + \frac{c_2}{t^2} + \cdots \right] \tag{19.1}$$

with the property of diverging for all finite t, play an important role in the theory of linear differential equations. Since series of this type arise throughout all of analysis, it follows that it is worth devoting some time and attention to the problem of establishing a secure basis for the use of these series. It turns out that in most important situations, these series can be manipulated with the same ease as convergent series.

If the series in (19.1) converged for large t, we would have the relations

$$\lim_{t \to \infty} u(t) = c_0 ,$$

$$\lim_{t \to \infty} t(u(t) - c_0) = c_1 ,$$

$$\vdots$$

$$\lim_{t \to \infty} t^n \left(u(t) - c_0 - \frac{c_1}{t} - \cdots - \frac{c_{n-1}}{t^{n-1}} \right) = c_n , \tag{19.2}$$

for $n = 0, 1, \cdots$.

We now take this relation as a defining relation connecting the function $u(t)$ and the sequence $c_0, c_1, \cdots$, and call the series

$$S(t) = c_0 + \frac{c_1}{t} + \frac{c_2}{t^2} + \cdots , \tag{19.3}$$

the *asymptotic series* associated with the function $u(t)$. We indicate this correspondence by the notation

$$u(t) \sim c_0 + \frac{c_1}{t} + \cdots + \frac{c_n}{t^n} + \cdots. \tag{19.4}$$

EXERCISES

19.1. Show that this equivalence relation possesses the following desirable properties:

(a) $u(t) \sim c_0 + \frac{c_1}{t} + \cdots, \qquad v(t) \sim b_0 + \frac{b_1}{t} + \cdots$

implies that

$$a_1 u + a_2 v \sim (a_1 c_0 + a_2 b_0) + \frac{a_1 c_1 + a_2 b_1}{t} + \cdots$$

for any constants a_1 and a_2 .

(b) The asymptotic series for uv is given by

$$uv \sim c_0 b_0 + \frac{c_0 b_1 + c_1 b_0}{t} + \cdots.$$

(c) If $c_0 \neq 0$, then $1/u(t)$ possesses an asymptotic series that is found by operating in the obvious fashion on the series $S(t)$.

(d) Show that the relations in (19.2) are equivalent to the statement that a sequence of constants $\{m_n\}$ exist with the property that

$$\left| u(t) - c_0 - \frac{c_1}{t} - \cdots - \frac{c_{n-1}}{t^{n-1}} \right| < \frac{m_n}{t^n}$$

for large t, and $n = 0, 1, 2, \cdots$.

(e) If

$$u(t) \sim \frac{c_2}{t^2} + \frac{c_3}{t^3} + \cdots,$$

then

$$\int_t^\infty u(s)\, ds \sim \frac{c_2}{t} + \frac{c_3}{2t^2} + \cdots.$$

(f) If we have both asymptotic relations

$$u(t) \sim c_0 + \frac{c_1}{t} + \frac{c_2}{t^2} + \cdots,$$

$$u'(t) \sim \frac{a_2}{t^2} + \frac{a_3}{t^3} + \cdots,$$

then $a_2 = -c_1$, $a_3 = -2c_2$, and so on.

(g) By consideration of $u = e^{-t} \sin e^{2t}$ show that

(1) all of the coefficients c_i can be zero without $u(t)$ necessarily being zero.

(2) u can have an asymptotic series without ensuring the existence of an asymptotic series for $u'(t)$.

19.2. Extend the equivalence relation in the following way:

$$u \sim g(t) \left[c_0 + \frac{c_1}{t} + \cdots \right]$$

means that

$$\frac{u}{g(t)} \sim c_0 + \frac{c_1}{t} + \cdots$$

if $g(t) \neq 0$ for large t, or that

$$\left| u - g(t) \left[c_0 + \frac{c_1}{t} + \cdots + \frac{c_{n-1}}{t^{n-1}} \right] \right| \leq \frac{m_n}{t^n}$$

for a sequence of constants m_n, if $|g(t)|$ is uniformly bounded for large t. Show that all of foregoing results hold with suitable restrictions upon $g(t)$.

19.3. Establish the laws of recurrence in the asymptotic expansion of the solutions of

(a) $u'' + \left(1 + \frac{1}{t^2} \right) u = 0$,

(b) $u'' - \left(1 + \frac{1}{t} \right) u = 0$,

(c) $u' + t^2 u = 0$.

19.4. Consider the problem of minimizing the integral

$$J(u) = \int_0^1 (u^2 - u'^2) \, dt,$$

with the constraints $u(0) = c$, $u(1) = b$, and the problem of minimizing

$$J(u, \lambda) = \int_0^1 (u^2 + u'^2) \, dt + \lambda(u(1) - b)^2$$

with the constraint $u(0) = c$. As $\lambda \to \infty$, does $\min_u J(u, \lambda) \to \min_u J(u)$, and, if so, how rapidly? (Bellman-Dreyfus).

COMMENTS AND BIBLIOGRAPHY

Heaviside is reputed to have said, "Ah, this series is divergent. Now we can use it to obtain numbers!"

20. The Exponential Integral

As an example of an asymptotic series not derived from a differential equation, but rather directly from the analytic representation of the function, let us consider the exponential integral

$$E_i(x) = e^x \int_x^\infty \frac{e^{-t}\,dt}{t}. \tag{20.1}$$

Integrating by parts repeatedly, we obtain the equivalent relation

$$E_i(x) = \frac{1}{x} - \frac{1}{x^2} + \cdots \frac{(-1)^n\,n!\,e^x}{x^{n+1}} \int_x^\infty \frac{e^{-t}\,dt}{t^{n+1}}. \tag{20.2}$$

We could also proceed in the following fashion. Making the change of variable, $t = x + y$, we have

$$E_i(x) = \int_0^\infty \frac{e^{-y}\,dy}{x+y}. \tag{20.3}$$

Proceeding formally and writing

$$\frac{1}{x+y} = \frac{1}{x} - \frac{y}{x^2} + \cdots, \tag{20.4}$$

we obtain the asymptotic series expansion

$$E_i(x) \sim \frac{1}{x} - \frac{1}{x^2} + \cdots + \frac{(-1)^n\,n!}{x^{n+1}} + \cdots \tag{20.5}$$

upon integrating term by term.

How many terms should we take in the asymptotic expansion in order to obtain the best approximation to the value of $E_i(x)$ for a large value of x? The reader will note that we obtain the term $(n+1)!/x^{n+1}$ from $n!/x^n$ by multiplication by $(n+1)/x$. Hence as long as $x > n + 1$, it pays to continue to another term; if $x < n + 1$, we increase the error term.

If then $x = 10$, the error in stopping at the term $10!/10^{11}$ is essentially the smallest we can obtain in this way. Since, by Stirling's formula (a result we shall derive below),

$$10! \sim 10^{10} \, e^{-10} \, \sqrt{20\pi}, \tag{20.6}$$

we see that the error is of the order of magnitude

$$(62.8)^{1/2} \, e^{-10} \, 10^{-1} \cong (8) \, (10)^{-1} \, 10^{-4.343} > 10^{-5}. \tag{20.7}$$

This is a very unsatisfactory result. We would like at least ten significant figures for digital computer purposes.

EXERCISES

20.1. In a similar fashion, obtain the asymptotic series for the error function

$$\text{Erf}\,(x) = e^{x^2} \int_x^\infty e^{-t^2} \, dt.$$

20.2. Obtain an error estimate for the partial sums of the series in (20.5) using the identity

$$\frac{1}{x+y} = \frac{1}{x} - \frac{y}{x} + \cdots (-1)^n \frac{y^n}{x^{n+1}} + \frac{y^{n+1}/x^{n+2}}{x+y} \, .$$

21. The Laplace Transform

The technique of repeated integration by parts is one that can be employed whenever we possess a representation of the form

$$f(x) = \int_0^\infty e^{-xt} \, g(t) \, dt \tag{21.1}$$

and $g(t)$ is infinitely often differentiable. Thus

$$f(x) \sim \frac{g(0)}{x} + \frac{g'(0)}{x^2} + \cdots + \frac{g^{(n)}(0)}{x^n} + \cdots. \tag{21.2}$$

EXERCISES

21.1. Let $g(t)$ be a function of t that is convex for $t \geq 0$; that is, $g''(t) > 0$, with a minimum value at $t = a > 0$, $g(a) > 0$. Obtain the asymptotic estimate

$$\int_0^\infty e^{-xg(t)} \, dt \sim \frac{(2\pi)^{1/2} \, e^{-xg(a)}}{(xg''(a))^{1/2}} \, .$$

21.2. Consider the integral representation

$$\Gamma(x+1) = \int_0^\infty e^{-t} \, t^x \, dt.$$

Write $t = xy$, obtaining the relation

$$\Gamma(x+1) = x^{x+1} \int_0^\infty (ye^{-y})^x \, dy$$

and thus obtain Stirling's formula

$$\Gamma(x+1) \sim x^x e^{-x} \sqrt{2\pi x}$$

as $x \to \infty$.

21.3. To obtain a more precise approximation, write

$$\Gamma(x+1) = x^{x+1} \int_0^1 (ye^{-y})^x \, dy + x^{x+1} \int_1^\infty (ye^{-y})^x \, dy$$

and make the change of variable $u = ye^{-y}$ in each of the intervals $0 \leq y \leq 1$, $1 \leq y \leq \infty$. In this way we obtain the asymptotic series

$$\frac{\Gamma(x+1) \, x^{-x} e^x}{(2\pi x)^{1/2}} \sim 1 + \frac{1}{12x} + \cdots$$

and use the Lagrange expansion to obtain the precise form of the subsequent terms.

21.4. Obtain the asymptotic behavior of the function defined by the integral $\int_0^1 t^x (1-t)^{-a} \, dt$, $0 < a < 1$, as $x \to \infty$.

21.5. Write

$$\frac{1}{s+t} = \int_0^1 w^s w^{t-1} \, dw = \frac{1}{t} - \frac{s}{t} \int_0^1 w^{s-1} w^t \, dw$$

$$= \frac{1}{t} - \frac{s}{t(t+1)} + \cdots.$$

Under what conditions does the infinite series converge? When does it represent an asymptotic series and what is the order of approximation?

21.6. Using the foregoing series, write

$$E_i(x) = \int_0^\infty \frac{e^{-y}\, dy}{x+y} = \frac{1}{x} \int_0^\infty e^{-y}\, dy - \frac{1}{x(x+1)} \int_0^\infty y e^{-y}\, dy + \cdots.$$

What is the order of approximation?

21.7. Alternatively, proceed as follows:

$$\sum_{n=0}^\infty \frac{(-1)^n\, n!}{z^n} = \int_0^\infty \frac{e^{-tz}}{1+t}\, dt.$$

Write

$$e^{-t} = 1 - r, \qquad t = \log\left(\frac{1}{1-r}\right),$$

so that

$$\sum_{n=0}^\infty \frac{(-1)^n\, n!}{z^n} = \int_0^1 \frac{(1-r)^{z-1}\, dr}{1 + \log\,(1/1-r)}.$$

Write

$$\frac{1}{1 + \log\,(1/1-r)} = 1 + \sum_{n=1}^\infty b_n r^n,$$

and then integrate term by term. (See E. T. Whittaker and G. N. Watson, *Modern Analysis*, pp. 142-144, for a rigorous discussion of this type of expansion.)

21.8. Use the Laplace transform to obtain contour integral representations of the solutions of $tu'' - u = 0$.

COMMENTS AND BIBLIOGRAPHY

For a detailed discussion of asymptotic series of the foregoing type, see the following books:

N. G. deBruijn, *Asymptotic Methods in Analysis*, Amsterdam, 1958.

G. Szegö, "Orthogonal Polynomials," *Amer. Math. Soc. Colloq. Publ.*, Vol. 23, 1939.

G. N. Watson, Bessel Functions, London: Cambridge University Press, 1922.

Many elegant results pertaining to asymptotic behavior in general will be found in these works, as well as many additional references.

To obtain results superior to those derived directly from divergent series, we must turn to continued fractions. These matters are discussed extensively in

Y. K. Luke, "The Padé Table and the τ-Method," *J. Math. and Phys.*, **37**, 1958.

See also

R. Bellman, "On Approximate Expressions for the Exponential Integral and the Error Function," *J. Math. and Phys.*, **30**, 226-231, 1952.

R. Bellman and J. M. Richardson, "A New Formalism in Perturbation Theory using Continued Fractions," *Proc. Nat. Acad. Sci. USA*, **48**, 1913-1915, 1962.

The theory of asymptotic series was created independently by Stieltjes and Poincaré, Stieltjes in connection with his study of the moment problem and continued fractions and Poincaré in connection with his research in the field of differential equations. See R. Bellman, *Stability Theory of Differential Equations*, New York: McGraw-Hill Book Company, Inc., 1953, for further discussion and references, and the book by Erdelyi quoted above.

Subject Index

Author Index

117